LANGUAGE ARTS KINDERG...
GETTING READY TO READ
Student Book 1

Contents

Lessons 1-10 1

Lessons 11-20 22

Lessons 21-30 42

Lessons 31-40 62

Lessons 41-50 82

Lessons 51-60 102

Lessons 61-70 122

Lessons 71-80 142

Writing Practice |162

Story Log |192

Story Book | 196

Author:
Mary Ellen Quint, Ph.D.

Editor:
Alan Christopherson, M.S.

Media Credits:
Page 11: © bluebearry, iStock, Thinkstock; **54, 111, 133:** © Suomuurain, iStock, Thinkstock; **83, 144, 145, 150, 151, 157** © IvanNikulin, iStock, Thinkstock; **91:** © Robertas Pėžas, iStock, Thinkstock; **115:** © palau83, iStock, Thinkstock; © AlexanderPokusay, iStock, Thinkstock; **121:** © colematt, iStock, Thinkstock; Ingram Publishing, iStock, Thinkstock; **127:** © Andrew Rybalko, iStock, Thinkstock; **139:** © reportman1985, iStock, Thinkstock; © clairevis, iStock, Thinkstock; **154:** © human, iStock, Thinkstock.

Animal Alphabet letters © IvanNikulin, iStock, Thinkstock.

804 N. 2nd Ave. E.
Rock Rapids, IA 51246-1759

How about you?

Do you want to read?

Words I can read.

More words I know.

We have names.

Sam and Jip

You have a name.

_____

- -

_____

Letters have names, too!

Say the letter names <u>after</u> your teacher.

a b c d e f g h i

j k l m n o p q r

s t u v w x y z

Say the names <u>with</u> your teacher. The letters all together are called the alphabet.

The alphabet comes in big and small.

Say the letter names again with capitals.

A B C D E F G

H I J K L M N

O P Q R S T U

V W X Y Z

Hurray! You did it! Practice often until you know them!

Letters big and letters small,
you can learn to write them all.

Practice circles.

Oo

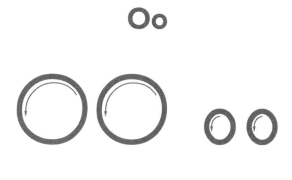

We read words from left to right.

We print words from left to right.

Draw a line from left to right.

→

Practice lines.

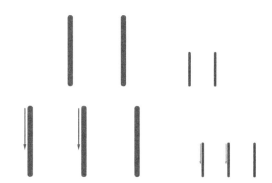

Practice circles and lines.

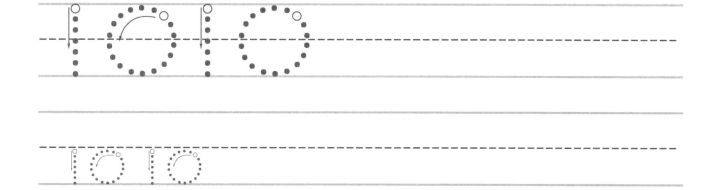

a b c d e f g h i
j k l m n o p q r
s t u v w x y z

Letters have names.
You can say them.

cat   hat   dog

All things have names.
Let's learn how to read them!

Write a A.

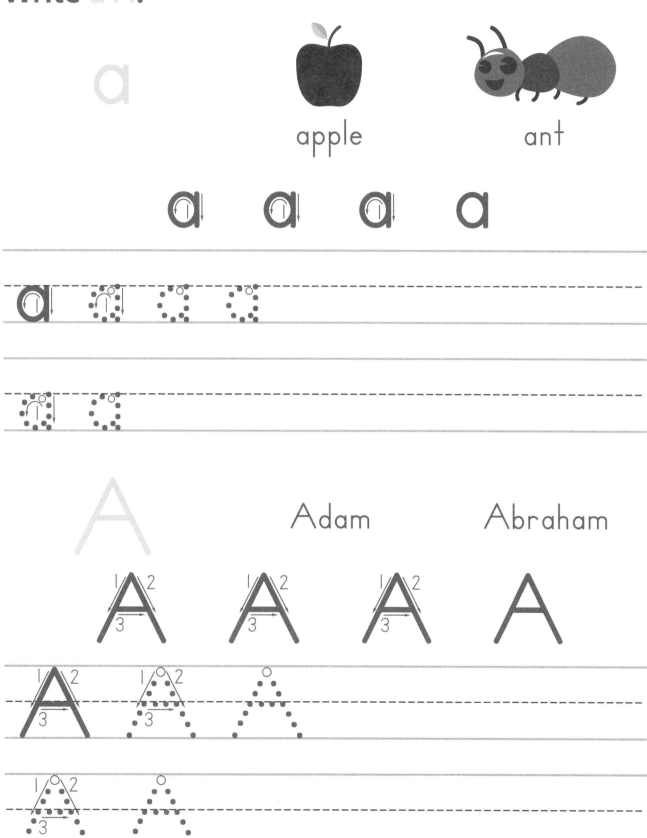

apple

ant

Adam

Abraham

How does short /a/ sound?

apple

man

cat

Sam

hat

Dad

Listen for short /a/.
Can you find more?

My Aa page.

Draw a line from left to right.

SHAPES

All things have a shape.

Special shapes have names.

Say the name of the shape <u>with</u> your teacher.

Look at the name of each shape.

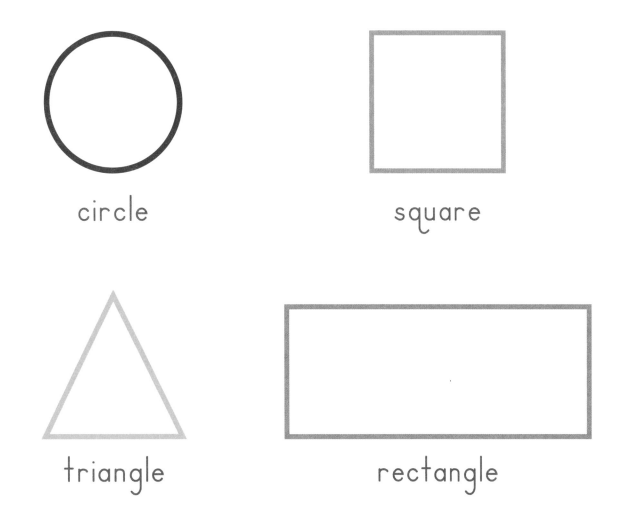

circle

square

triangle

rectangle

Match the shapes.

Write b B.

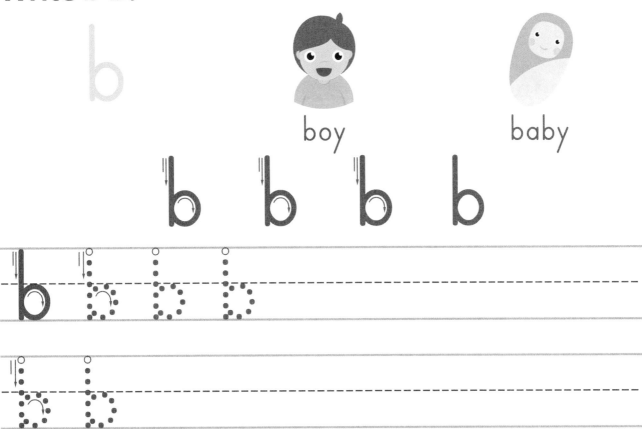

boy

baby

Bible

Bethlehem

Bb

What sound does <u>b</u> make?

box   ball   bed

bow   baby   bird

Listen for <u>b</u>.

Can you find more?

My Bb page.

Match the shapes.

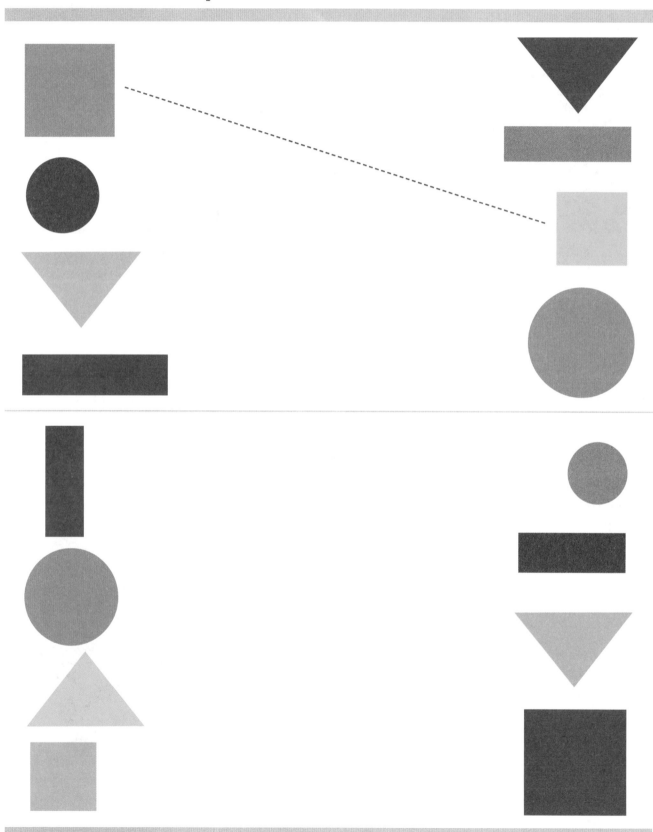

COLORS

Colors are everywhere.

Colors have names.

Say the name of each color <u>with</u> your teacher.

Look at the name of each color.

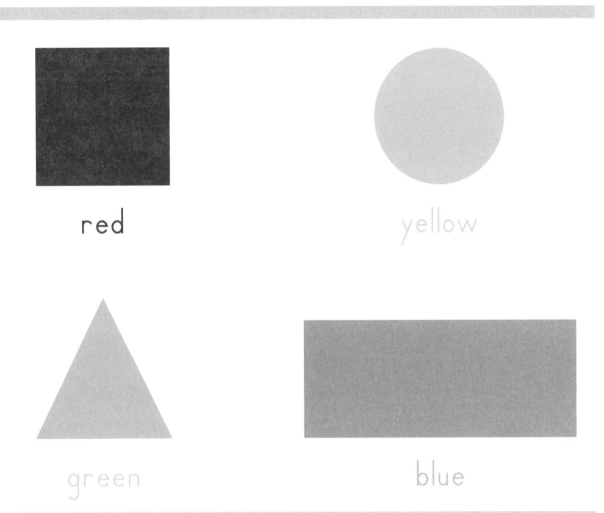

red

yellow

green

blue

Match the colors.

yellow

red

green

blue

Match the colors and shapes.

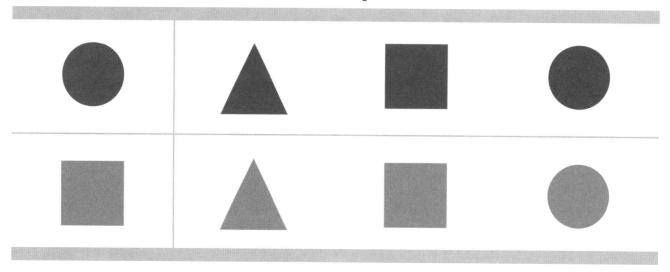

Practice t T.

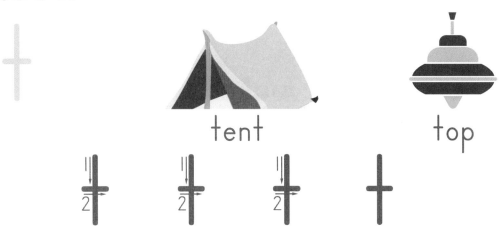

tent   top

Thomas   Timothy

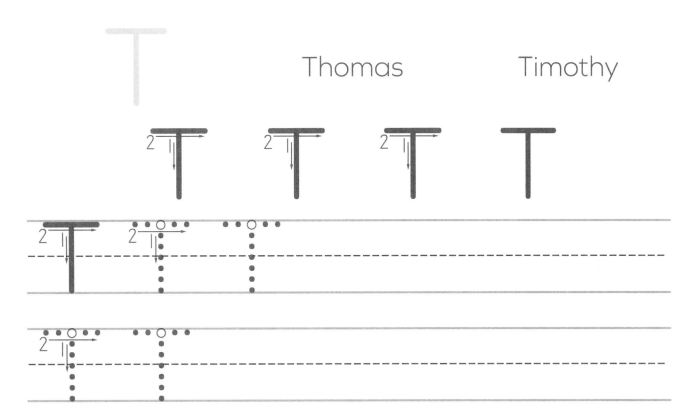

What sound does <u>t</u> make?

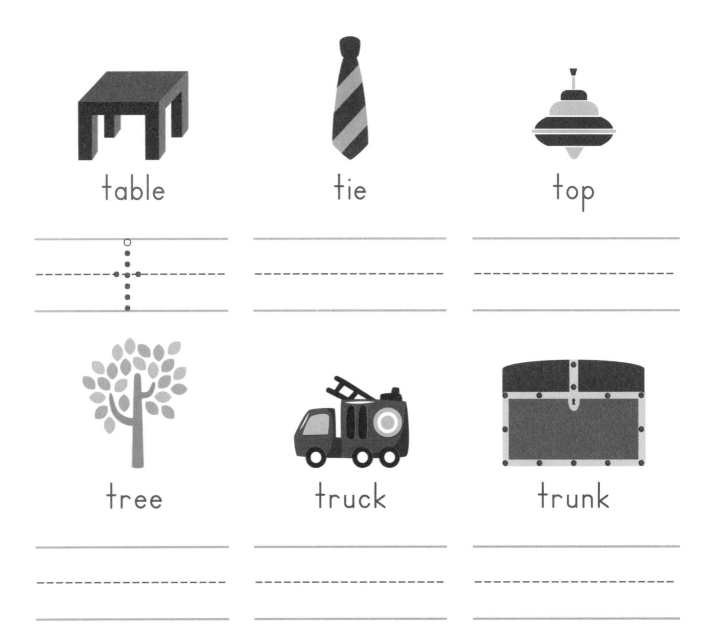

table

tie

top

tree

truck

trunk

Listen for <u>t</u>.

Can you find more?

My Tt page.

Listen and find.

Practice m M.

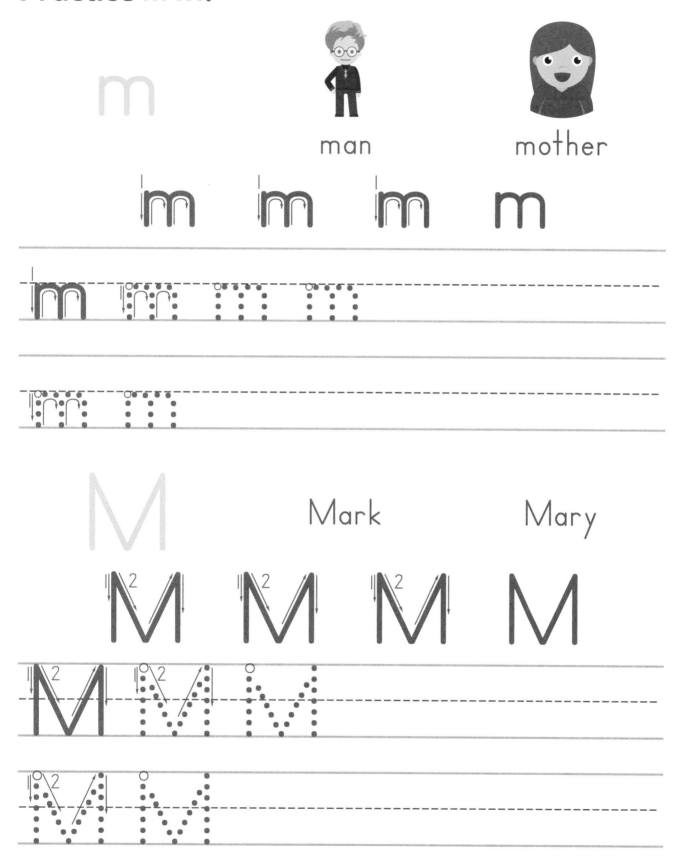

man

mother

m   m   m   m

Mark   Mary

M M M M

Mm

What sound does <u>m</u> make?

Does it remind you of something good?

milk

moon

mouse

monkeys

mail

man

Listen for <u>m</u>.

Can you find more?

My Mm page.

Circle the shapes.

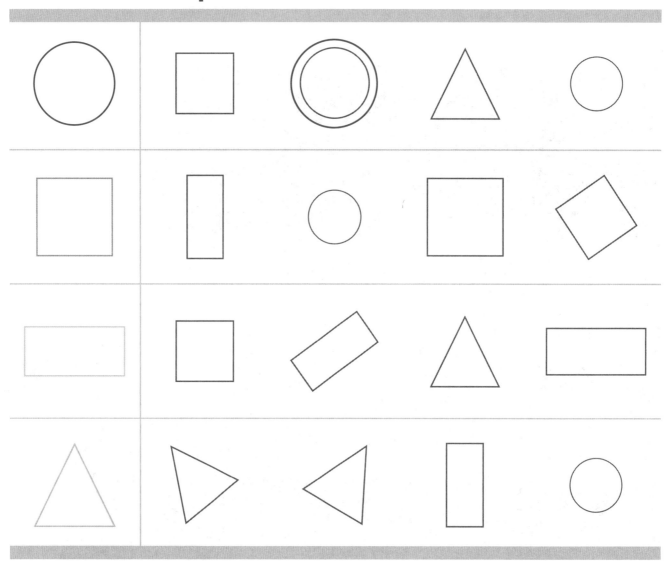

Color the 🔴 red.

Color the ▪ blue.

Color the ▲ green.

Color the ▬ yellow.

Circle the pictures.

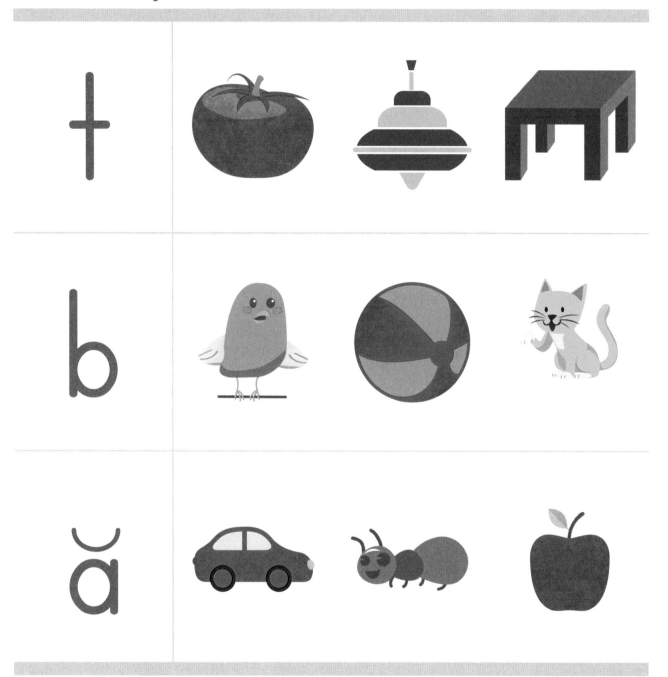

Put an X on the picture.

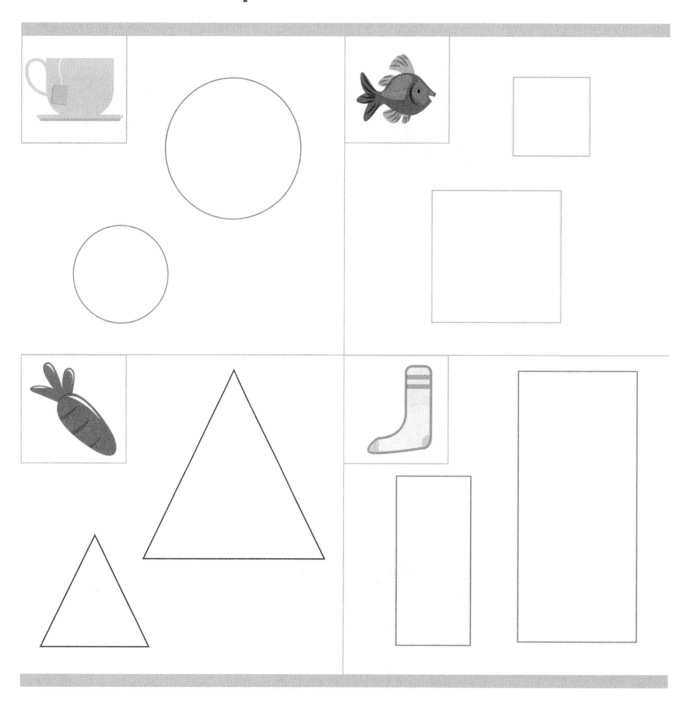

Practice r R.

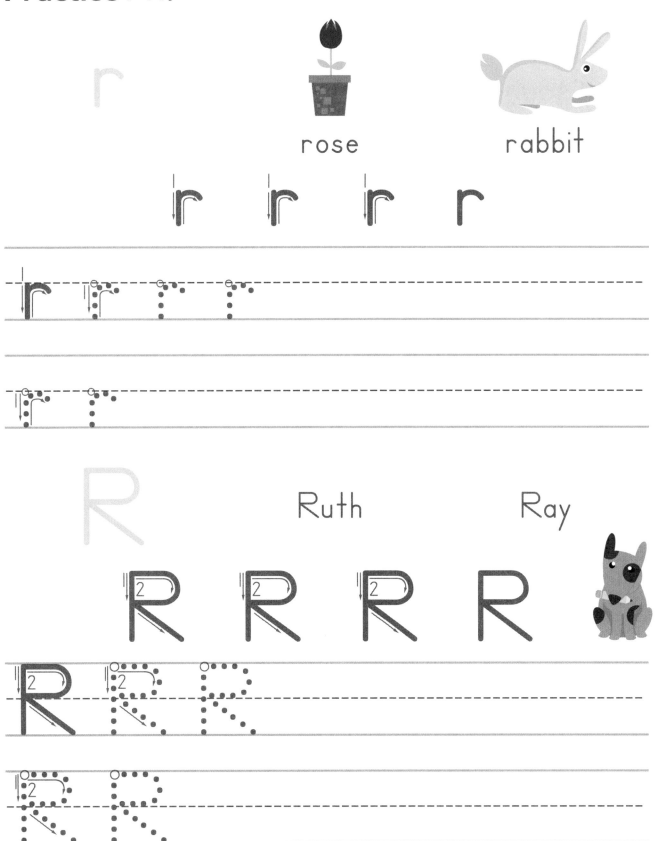

rose

rabbit

r r r r r

R

Ruth   Ray

R R R R

What sound does <u>r</u> make?

rake

rooster

rain

rainbow

rug

radio

Listen for <u>r</u>.
Can you find more?

My Rr page.

Circle the shapes.

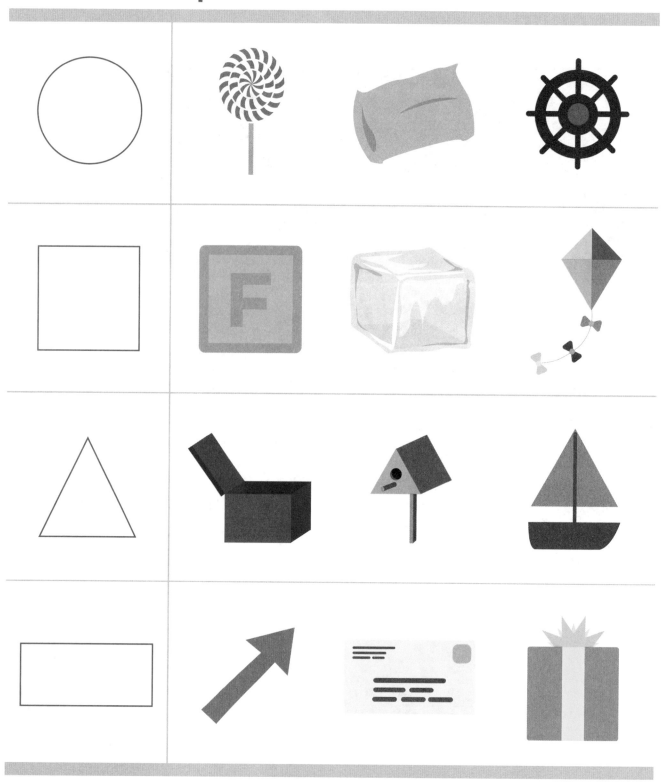

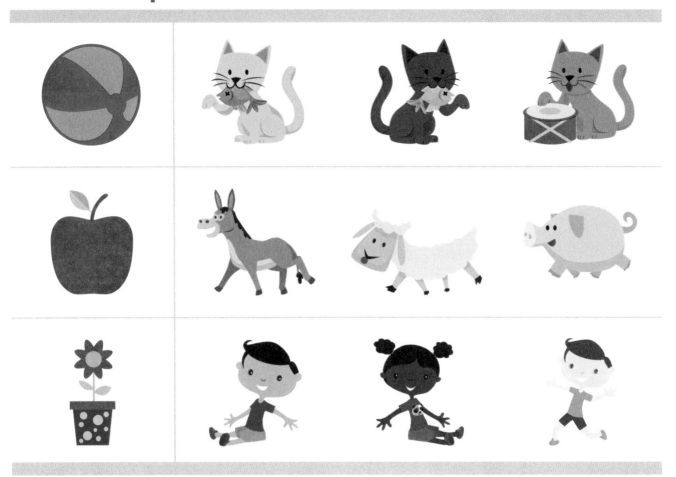

Circle the picture.

Circle the letter.

a	b	m	a	r
m	r	b	m	a
r	a	r	b	m

Write the letter. Circle the picture.

r _ _ _ _ _ _ _ _ _ _

t _ _ _ _ _ _ _ _ _ _

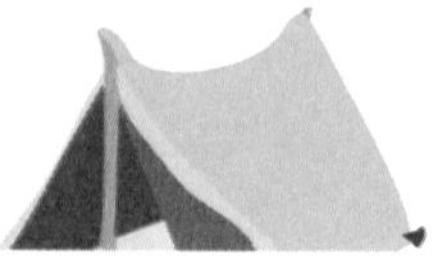

m _ _ _ _ _ _ _ _ _ _

b _ _ _ _ _ _ _ _ _ _

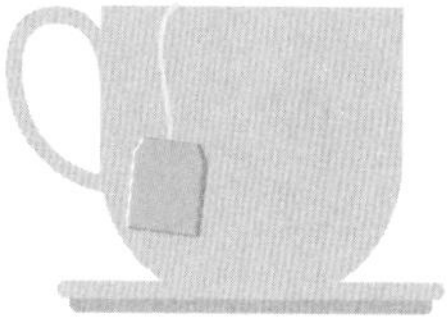

Practice e E.

egg

elephant

e e e e

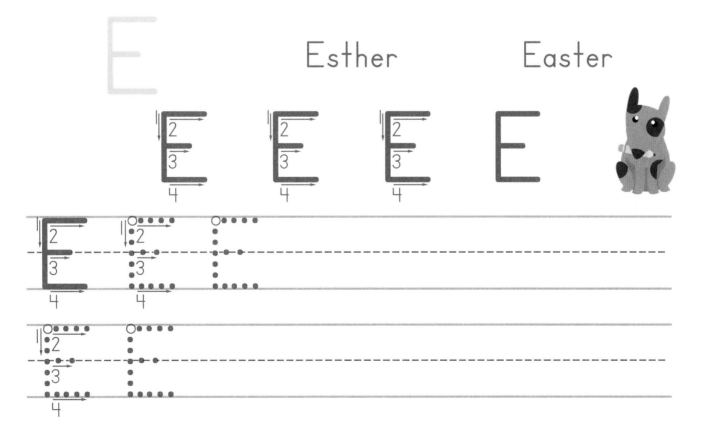

Esther

Easter

How does short /e/ sound?

envelope

pencil

bell

men

bed

10

ten

Listen for short /e/.
Can you find more?

My Ee page.

Read the alphabet to your teacher.

Circle the letters we have done.

Sing the alphabet song.

Circle the shapes.

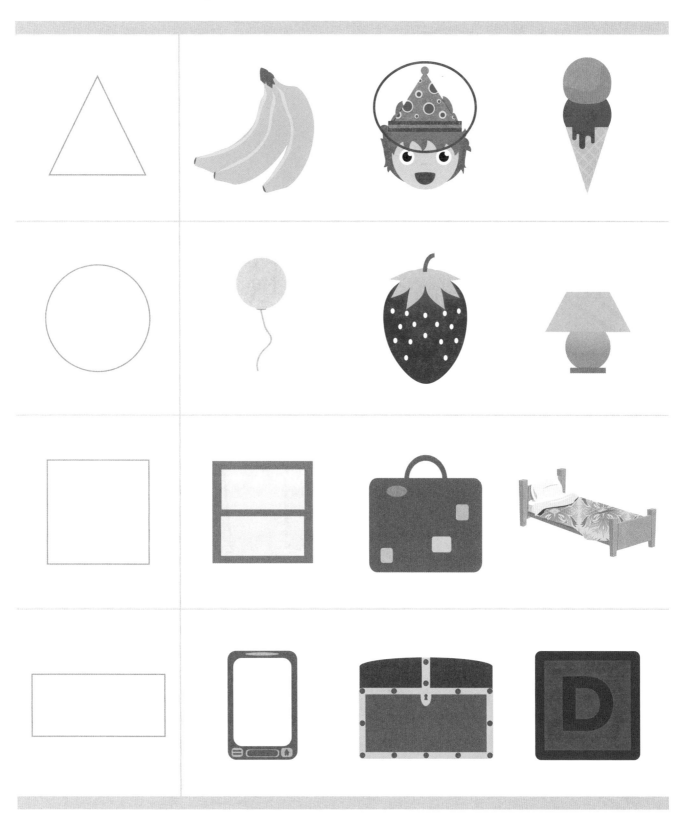

Color.

Practice s S.

soap

sun

    S S S S

Savior   Samson

S S S S

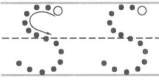

Ss

What sound does s make?

sock   seven   sailboat

Sam   snake   six

Listen for s.
Can you find more?

My Ss page.

Match the letters.

a	R	M	s
t	M	E	m
m	A	B	e
r	T	S	b

Circle the words.

a	an	so
b	at	bat
m	to	man
t	ran	to

I can make words
with the sounds
I know.

Try these.

at _____   am _____

sat _____   rat _____

I am Sam.

I sat at a .

I bat a) (.

A rat sat at a .

Can you make more?

Circle the picture.

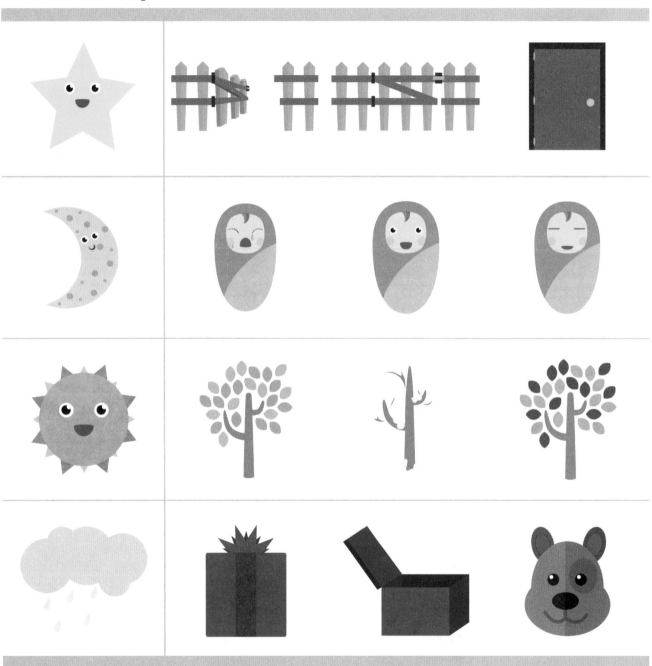

Write your name.

Practice n N.

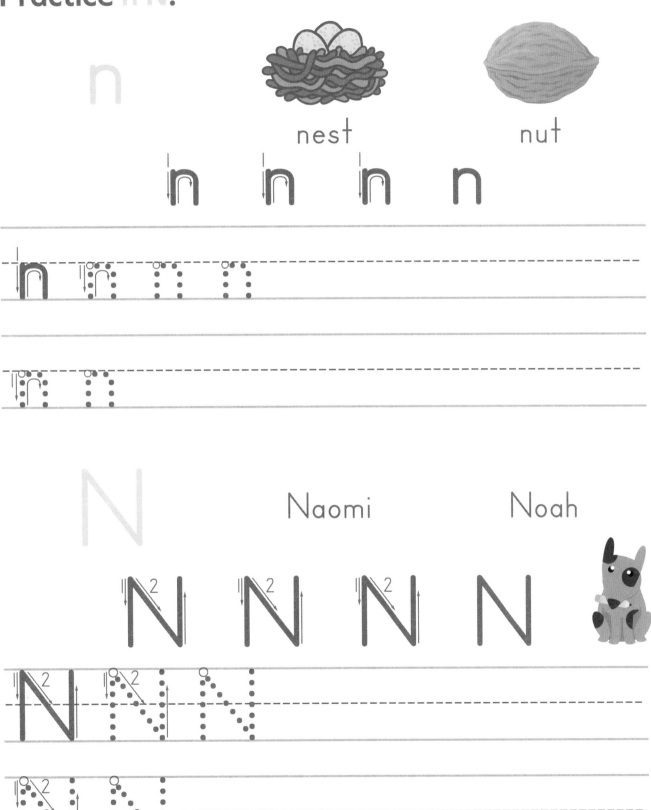

nest

nut

Naomi

Noah

What sound does <u>n</u> make?

net

nail

9

nine

newspaper

neck

numbers

Listen for <u>n</u>.

Can you find more?

My Nn page.

Make new words with the sound of /n/.

an   ----------------------   ran   ----------------------

----------------------   ----------------------

tan   ----------------------   fan   ----------------------

----------------------   **10**   ----------------------

Ann   ----------------------   Ben   ----------------------

Practice d D.

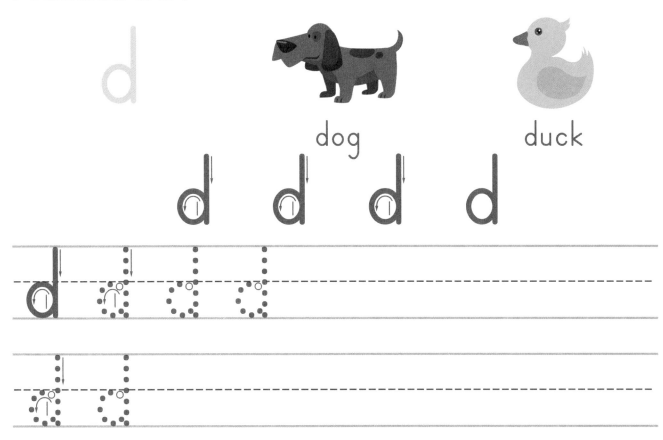

dog

duck

Daniel

David

Dd

What sound does d make?

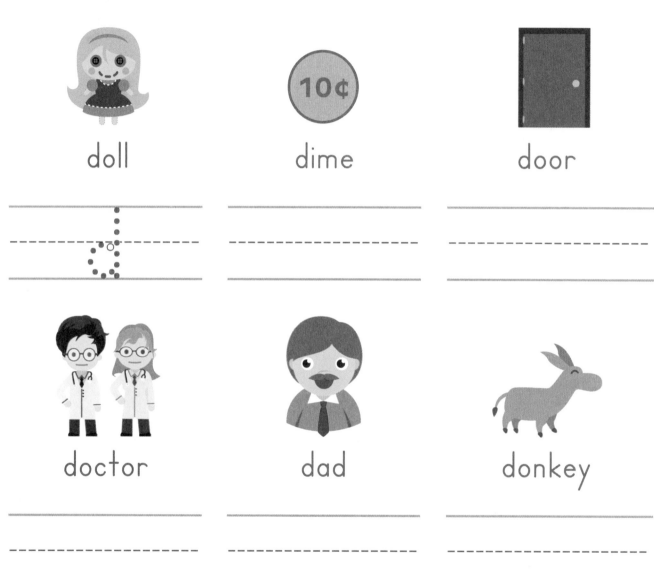

doll   dime   door

doctor   dad   donkey

Listen for d.

Can you find more?

My Dd page.

Try these short /a/ words.

Sam ---------------- ran ----------------

---------------- ----------------

Dad ---------------- rat ----------------

Ann and Dan ran.

Can you find more?

Practice p P.

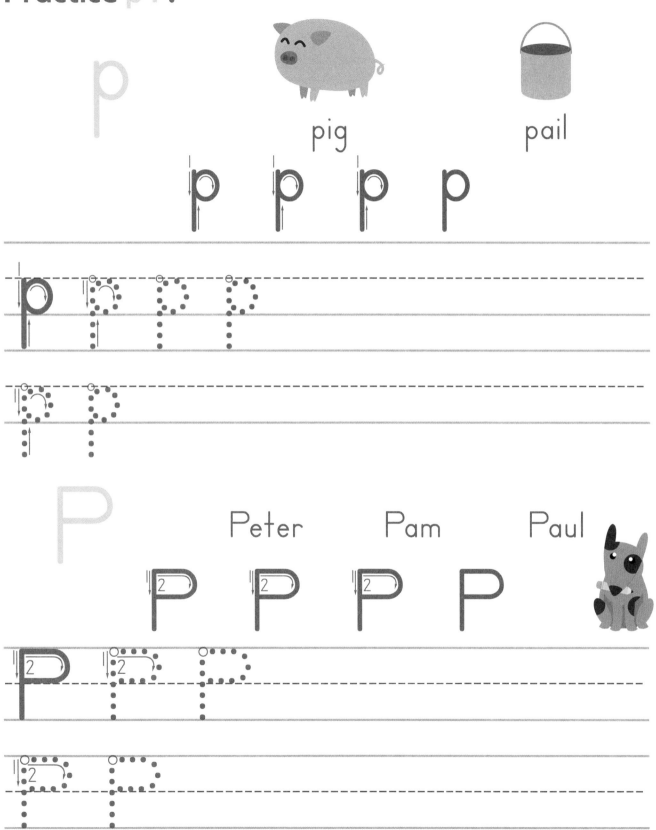

p

pig

pail

p p p p

p p p p

p p

P

Peter   Pam   Paul

P P P P

P P

P P

What sound does /p/ make?

picture

pillow

paintbrush

pumpkin

piano

pie

Listen for /p/.

Can you find more?

My Pp page.

Color the shapes, ●, ■, ▲, ▬.

Color

 red

 green

 blue

▲ yellow

Write the letter.
Circle the picture.

d			
n			
p			
s			

Try these short /e/ words.

men - - - - - - - - - - - - - - -   pen - - - - - - - - - - - - - - -

10 - - - - - - - - - - - - - - -

tent - - - - - - - - - - - - - - -   red - - - - - - - - - - - - - - -

Ben and Ted met ten men.
Can you find more?

Practice i I.

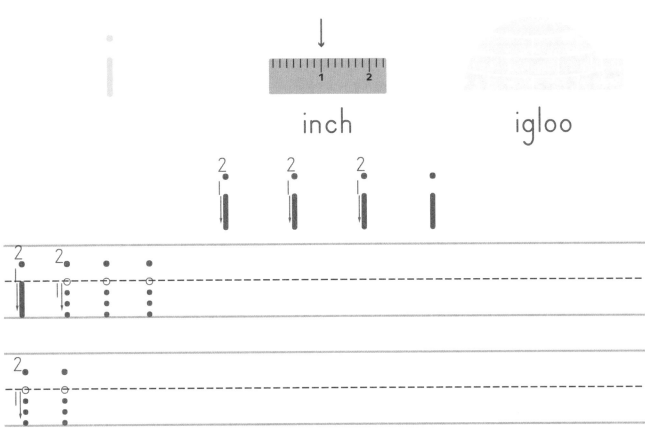

inch   igloo

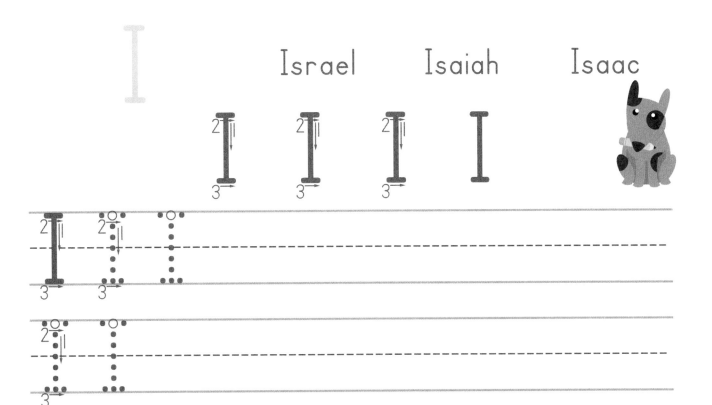

Israel   Isaiah   Isaac

How does short /i/ sound?

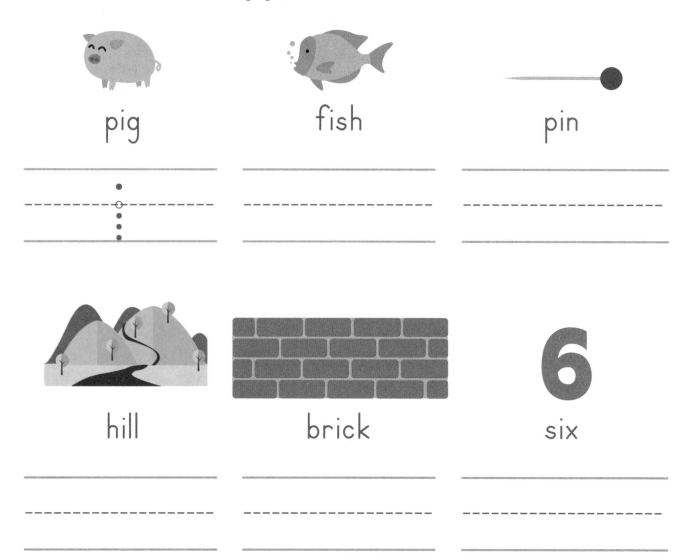

pig

fish

pin

hill

brick

6

six

Listen for short /i/.
Can you find more?

My Ii page.

Try these short /i/ words.

Jip ----------------

tip ----------------

pin ----------------

dip ----------------

bin ----------------

sip ----------------

sit ----------------

mitt ----------------

Circle the picture.

More color names.

brown

purple

pink

orange

Say the names with your teacher.

Practice l L.

l

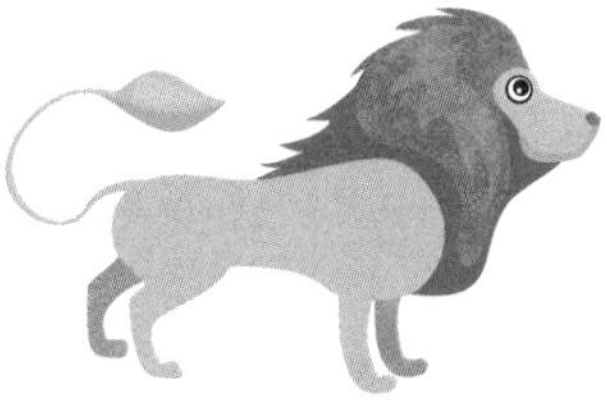

lion

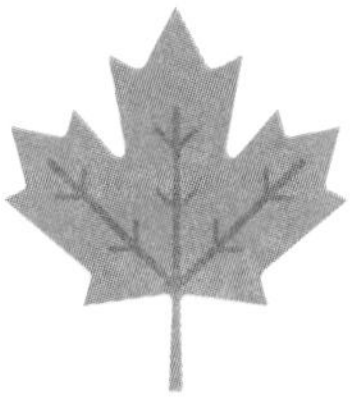

leaf

l l l l

L

Luke

Lord

L L L L

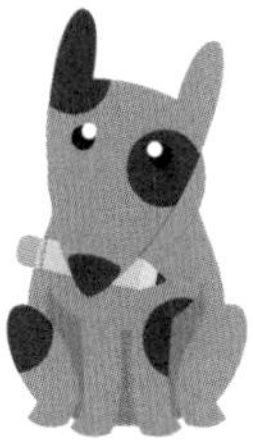

What sound does <u>l</u> make?

log

lemon

leg

letter

leaf

lamp

Listen for <u>l</u>.
Can you find more?

My Ll page.

Circle the shapes.

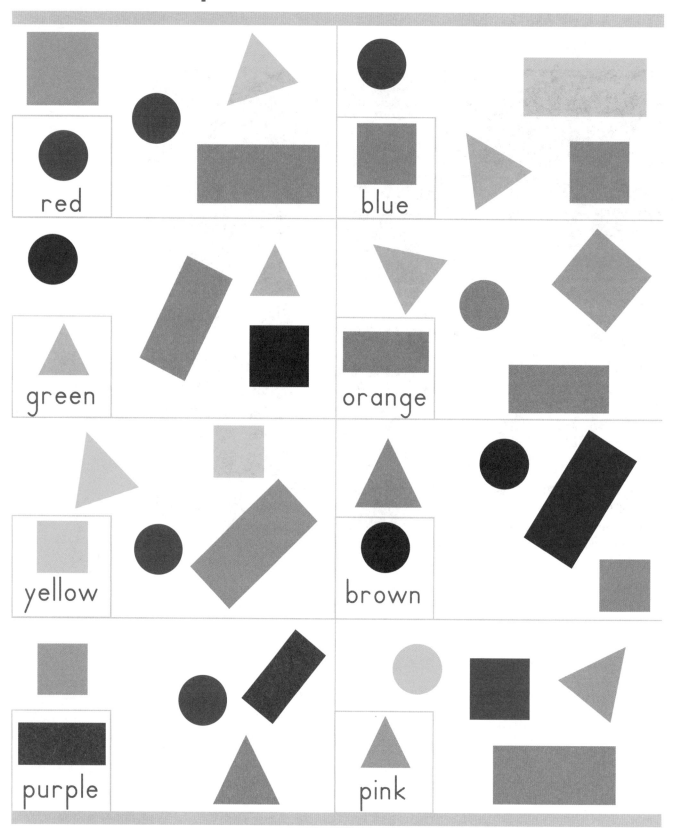

‑‑‑‑‑‑‑‑‑‑‑‑‑‑‑‑‑‑‑‑‑‑‑‑‑‑‑‑‑‑

Read the alphabet to your teacher.

a b c d e f g h i
j k l m n o p q r
s t u v w x y z

Write your name.

‑‑‑

‑‑‑

Circle the picture. Write the small letter.

l _____

p _____

d _____

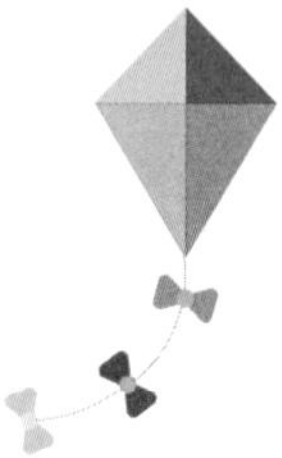

n _____

s _____

r _____

Match the letters.

R	b	n	L
T	m	d	P
M	r	l	D
B	t	p	N

Circle the pictures.

b		
m		
t	**10**	

Circle the pictures with short /a/, /e/, and /i/ sounds.

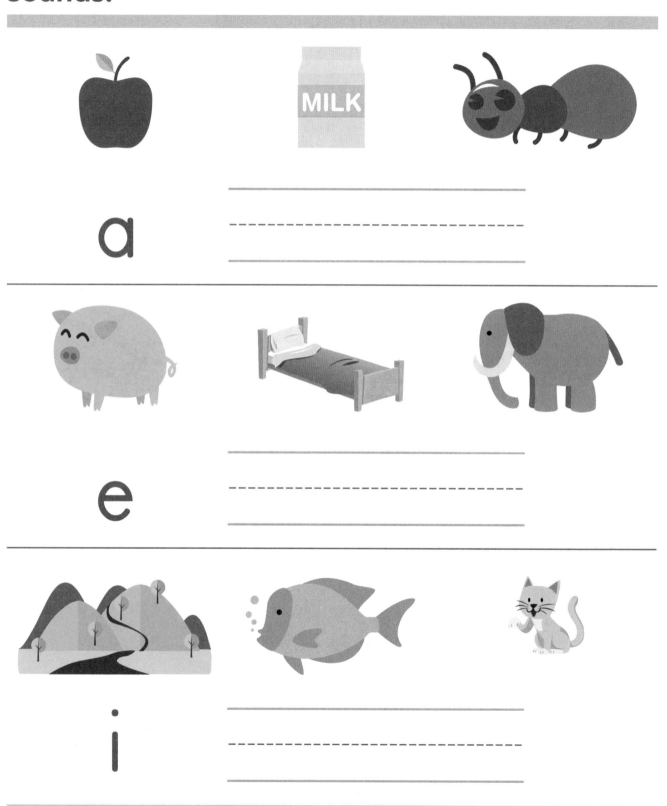

a

e

i

Practice k K.

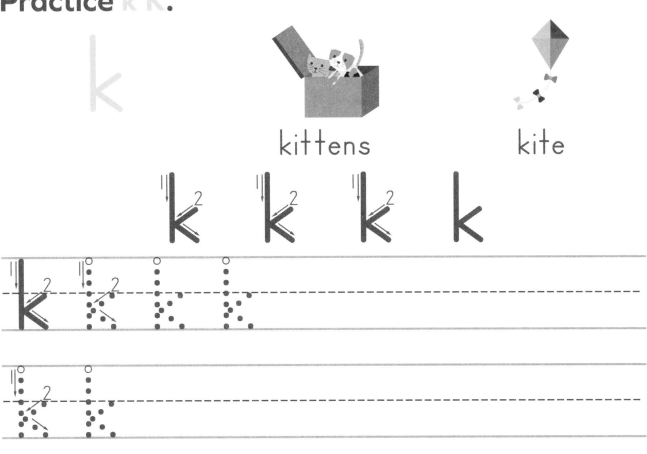

kittens   kite

Ken   Kathleen

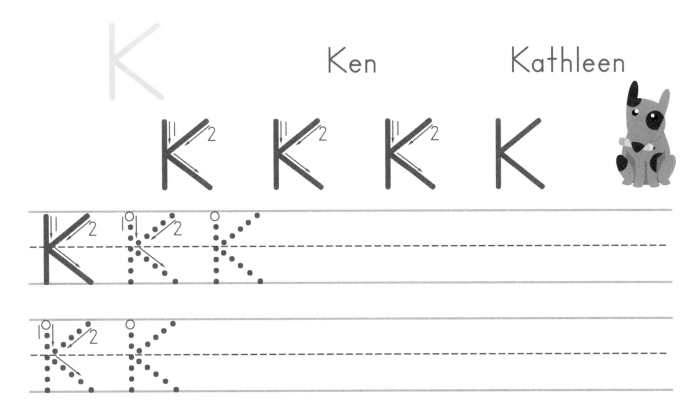

Kk

What sound does k make?

key

king

kite

kangaroo

kitten

kick

Listen for k.
Can you find more?

My Kk page.

K k

kangaroo

Look!

Circle the pictures.

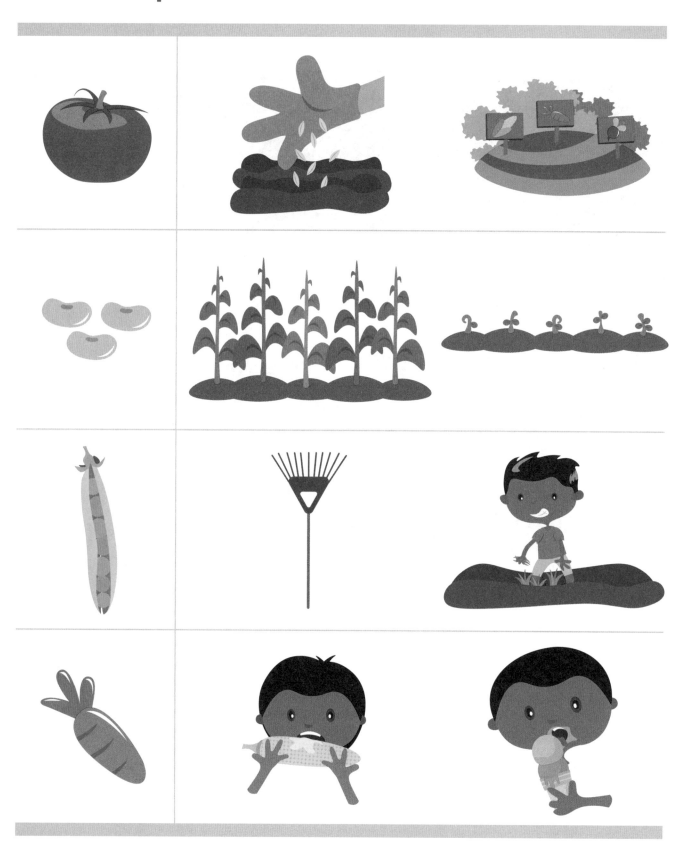

Practice c C.

carrot   cup

c c c c

Christ   Christmas   Carol

C C C C

What sound does c make?

corn

cat

candle

car

cake

cow

Listen for this c sound.
Does it sound like k?

Can you find more?

My Cc page.

clock

sock

lock

tack

duck

truck

Can you find more?

Practice f F.

f

fish

fan

f f f f

Father   Frank

F F F F

What sound does f make?

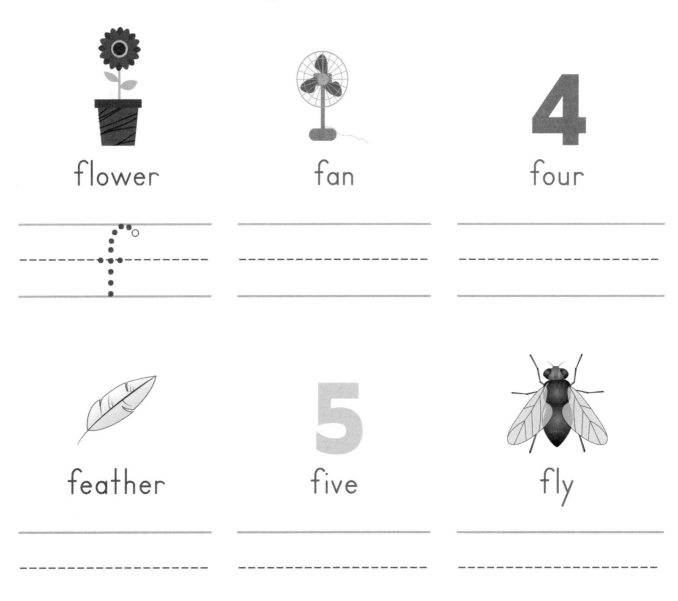

flower   fan   four

feather   five   fly

Listen for f.

Can you find more?

My Ff page.

Learn a new shape.

oval

Color the shapes.

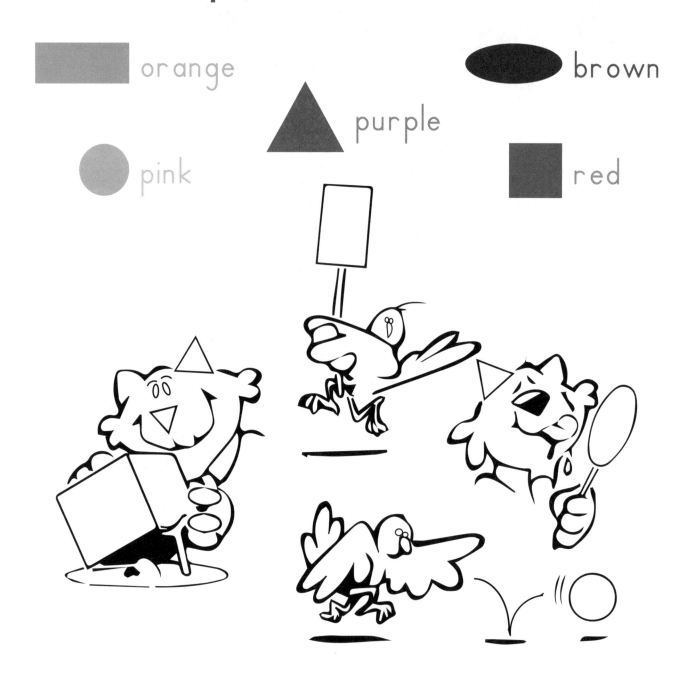

orange

pink

purple

brown

red

Match the letters.

a	d	a	B
b	a	b	A
d	b	d	D
e	c	c	E
c	e	e	C

Circle the letter.

a	e	o	r	(a)
b	d	p	g	b
c	c	o	s	a
d	p	g	q	d
e	i	o	c	e

Say the letter names.

a b c d e f

Write the missing letters.

a   ----------   c   d

c   ----------   e   f

a   b   ----------   d

Practice h H.

hen

hat

Helen

Henry

H is very quiet.
What sound does h make?
How does it feel?

hearts

hand

horse

hat

hair

house

Listen for h. Can you find more?

My Hh page.

Learn about size.

big

little

small

large

Circle the picture.

Say the letters.
Join the letters.
Color the picture.

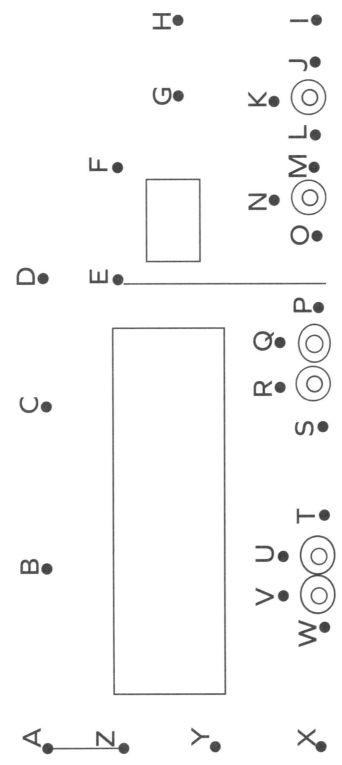

Circle the picture. Write the letter.

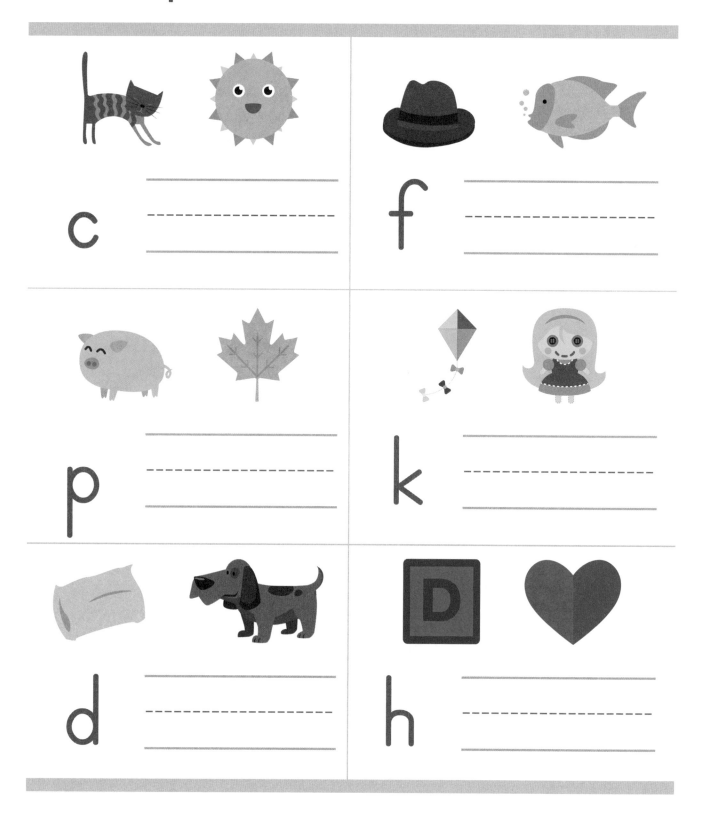

c

f

p

k

d

h

Practice o O.

ox

octopus

October   Oscar

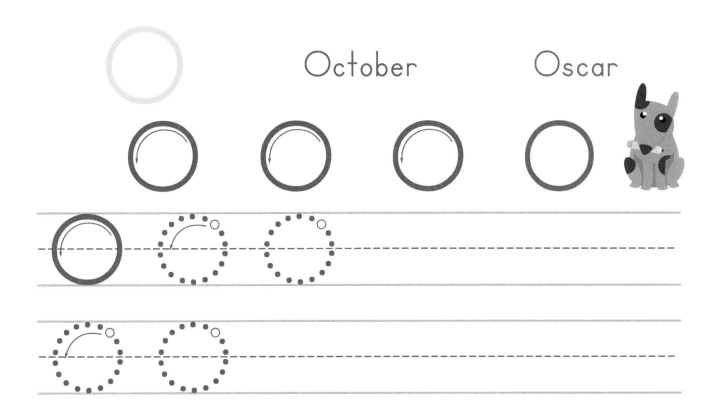

How does short /o/ sound?

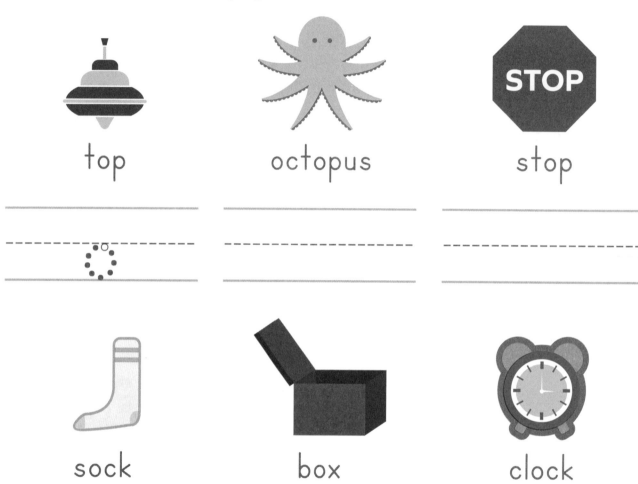

top

octopus

stop

sock

box

clock

Listen for short /o/.
Can you find more?

My Oo page.

Try these short /o/ words.

hot _____

top _____

got _____

fox _____

pot _____

clock _____

cot _____

block _____

Can you find more?

Draw the patterns.

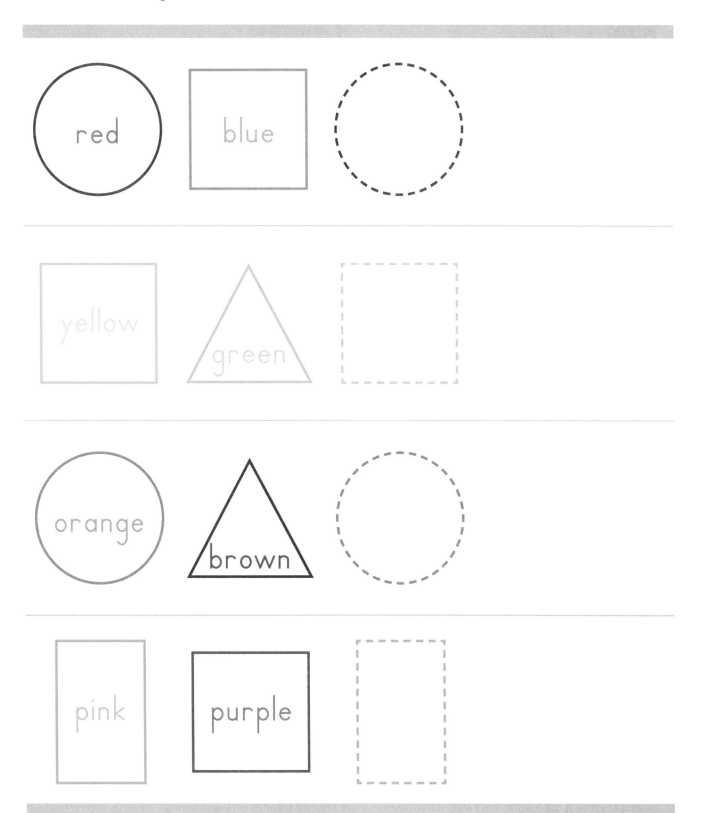

Circle the pictures.

Practice g G.

goat   girl

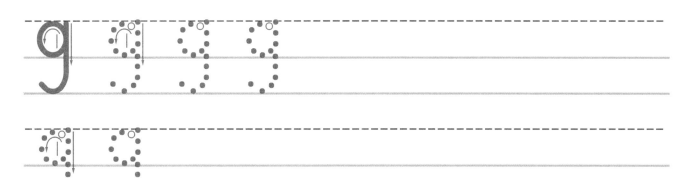

G   God   Gabriel

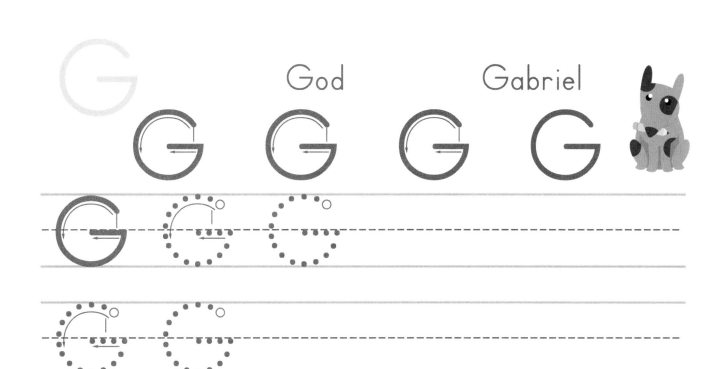

Gg

What sound does /g/ make here?

grapes

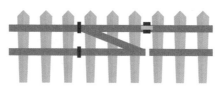

gate

garden

guitar

girl

gift

Listen for this /g/ sound.
Can you find more?

My Gg page.

Circle the letter.

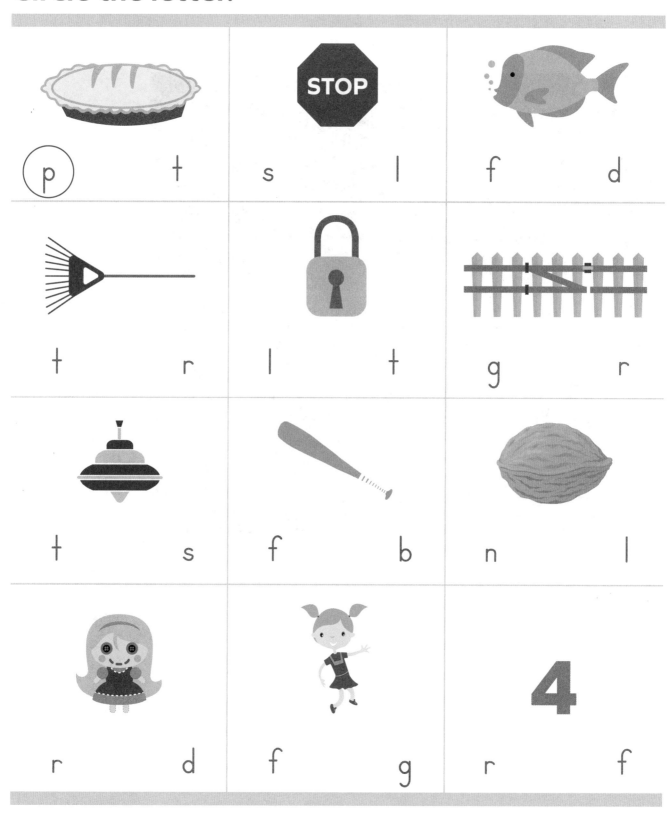

(p)   t

s   l

f   d

t   r

l   t

g   r

t   s

f   b

n   l

r   d

f   g

r   f

Where is it?

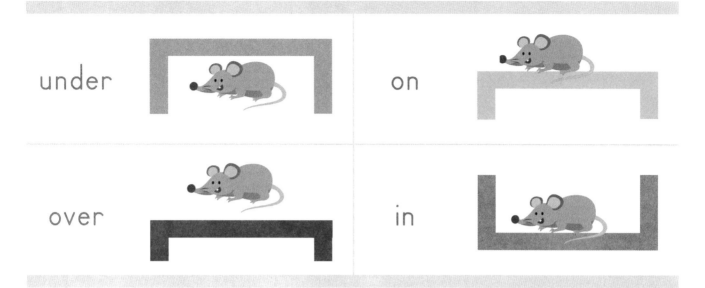

under

on

over

in

Circle the picture.

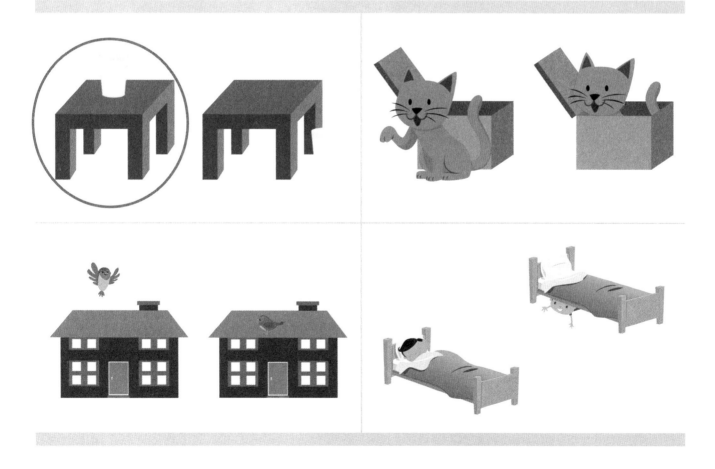

Say the letter names.

a b c d e f g h i

Write the missing letters.

e _____ g h

c d _____ f

f _____ h i

Practice j J.

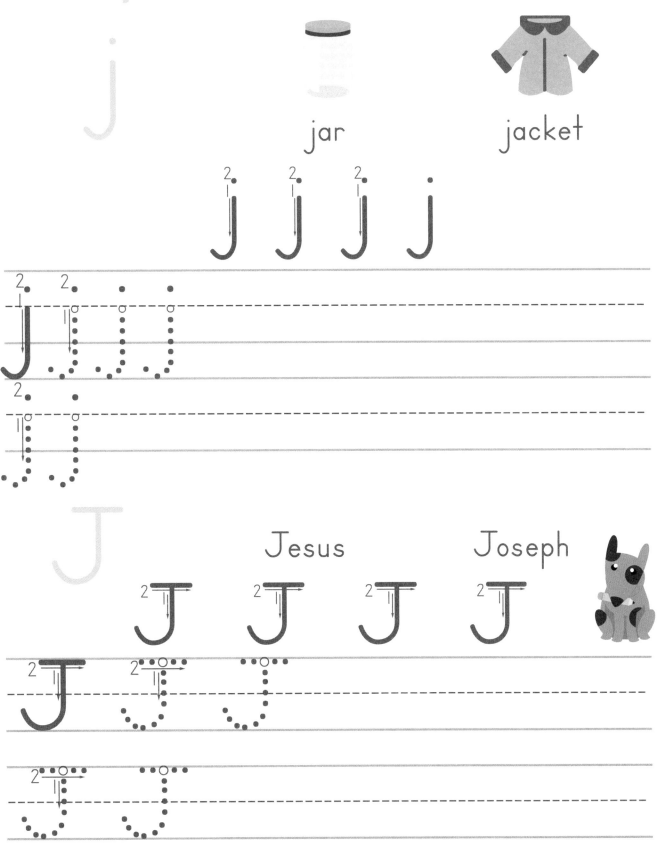

jar

jacket

Jesus

Joseph

What sound does /j/ make?

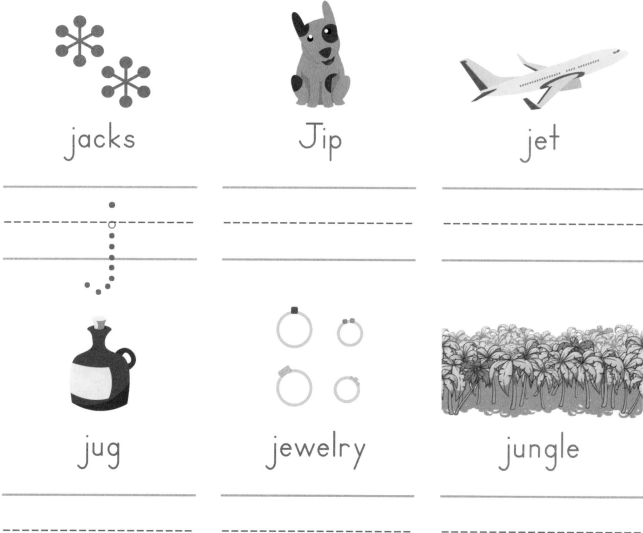

jacks

Jip

jet

jug

jewelry

jungle

Listen for /j/.
Can you find more?

My Jj page.

Write the missing letters.

a   _____   c   d

e   _____   _____   h

i   j   _____   l

_____   n   o   _____

Two more color names.

black   white

Match the colors.

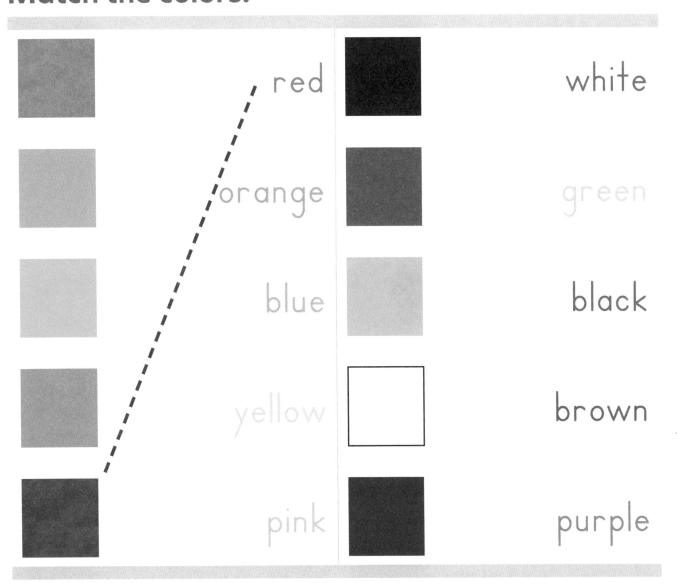

red

orange

blue

yellow

pink

white

green

black

brown

purple

Match the shapes.

Circle the pictures.

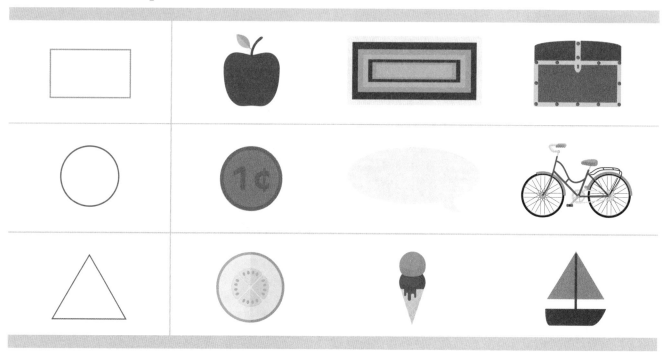

Practice v V.

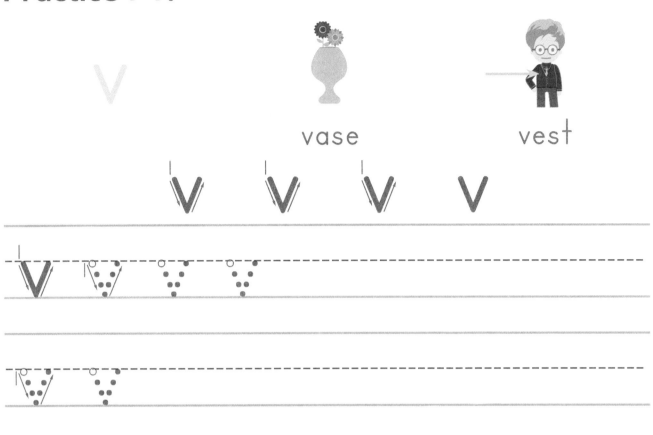

vase

vest

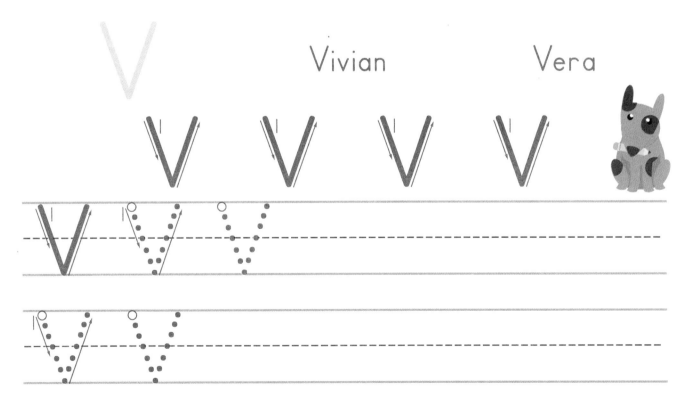

Vivian

Vera

What sound does <u>v</u> make?

vest

volcano

van

a e i
o u
vowels

vase

vine

Listen for <u>v</u>.
Can you find more?

My Vv page.

Circle the letter.

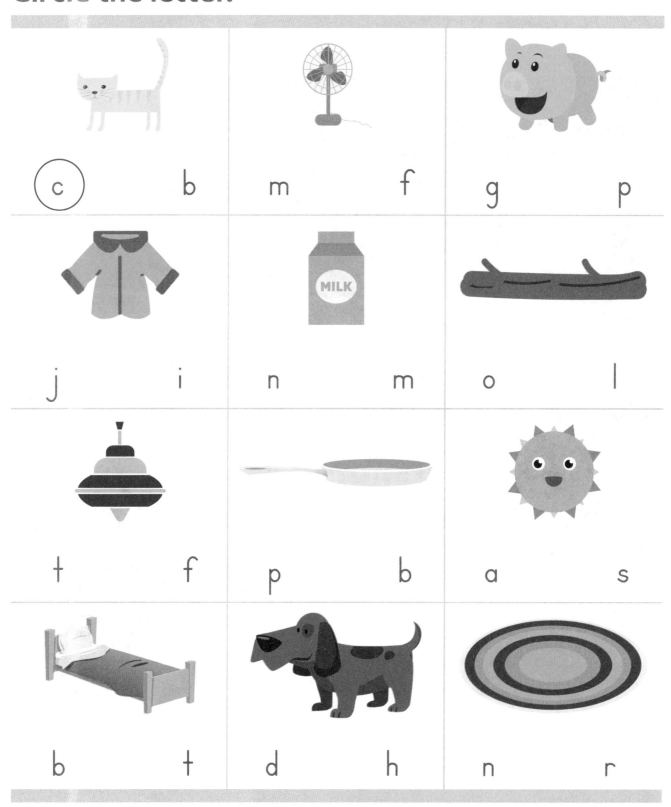

(c)   b   m   f   g   p

j   i   n   m   o   l

t   f   p   b   a   s

b   t   d   h   n   r

Circle the pictures.

Write your name.

Match the letters.

o	A	D	b
a	O	A	d
c	E	B	a
e	C	E	e

Circle the letter.

c	at	can	do
a	egg	dog	am
b	bat	and	at
o	an	oh	do
d	oh	do	an

Practice w W.

well

world

William

Wally

What sound does w make?

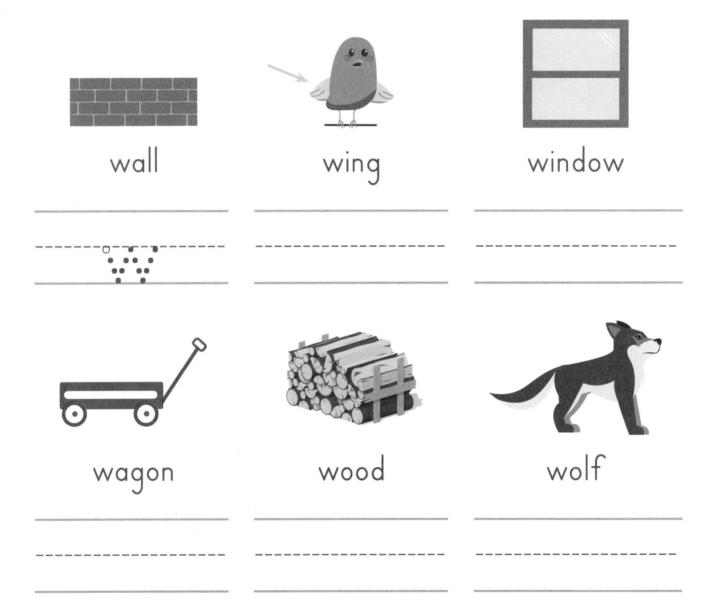

wall

wing

window

wagon

wood

wolf

Listen for w.

Can you find more?

My Ww page.

wombat

Look!

Circle the short vowel pictures.

a	cat	cup	man
e	bed	bell	hat
i	box	6	pig
o	STOP	hand	clock

Say the letters.
Join the letters.
Color the picture.

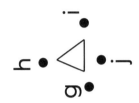

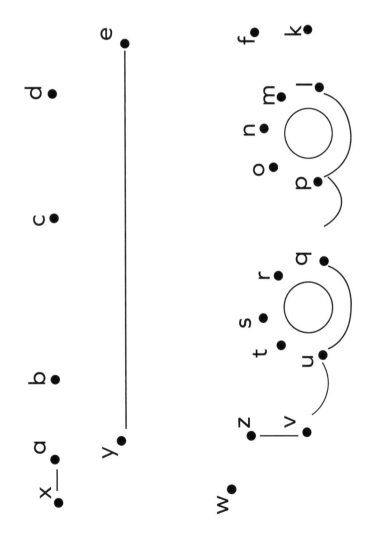

Circle the words.

i	(in)	lie	kit	it
l	he	look	is	land
t	at	the	two	how
n	no	me	not	can
L	He	Lee	It	Larry
T	Look	At	To	Tom
I	Is	Low	In	Time
N	My	No	Nancy	He

Match the letters.

t	N	O		d
l	I	B		o
n	T	D		b
i	L	C		n
e	A	T		c
a	E	N		t

Practice u U.

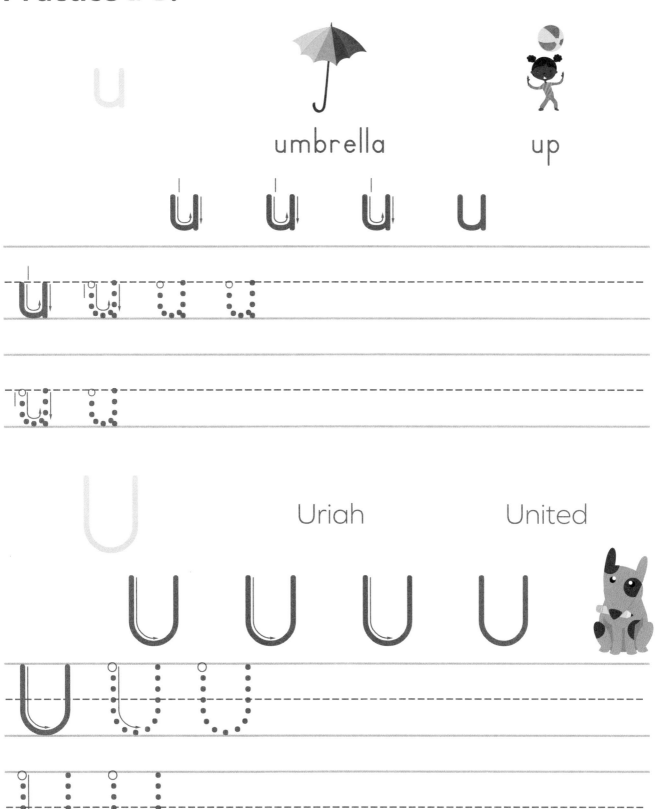

umbrella

up

Uriah

United

How does short /u/ sound?

up

cup

sun

umbrella

nut

truck

Listen for short /u/.
Can you find more?

My Uu page.

Try these short
/ʊ/ words.

tub ------------------

bug ------------------

mud ------------------

mug ------------------

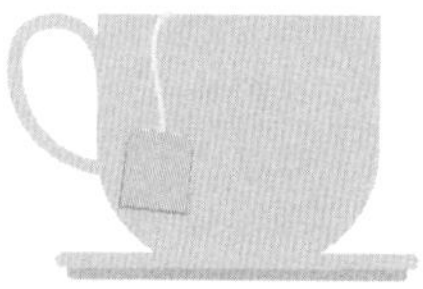

Can you find more?

Draw a line from left to right.

 - →

 I am running.

 I am running.

Write the word I.

------------- am running.

------------- can run fast.

------------- can pray.

Say the letter names.

r s t u v w

Write the missing letters.

r ---------- t u

t u ---------- w

r s ---------- u

Practice y Y.

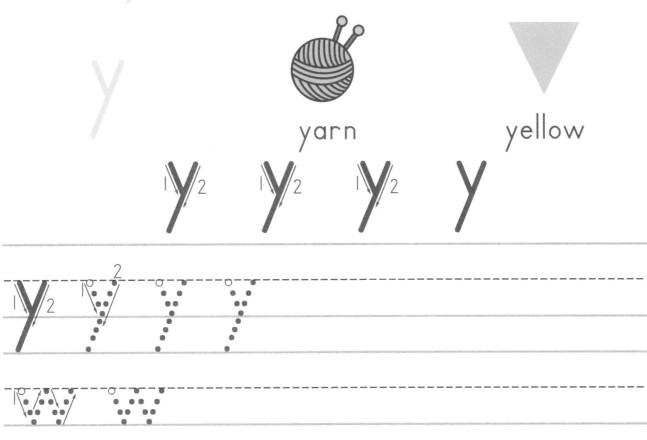

yarn   yellow

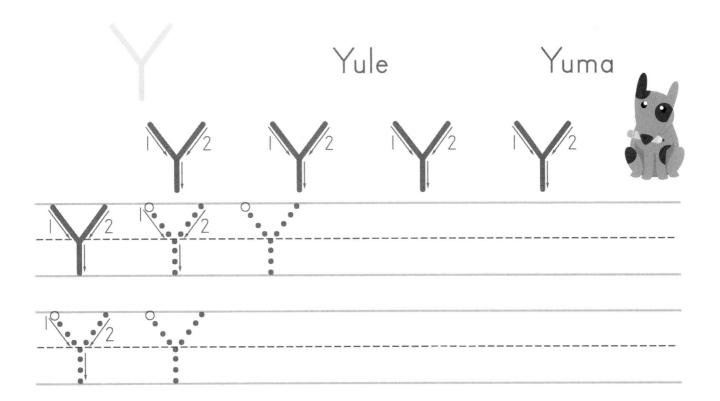

Yule   Yuma

Y y

What sound does /y/ make?

yo‾yo

yarn

year

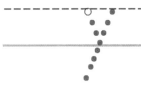

yard

yellow

Yes!

yes

Listen for /y/.

Can you find more?

My Yy page.

Color.

blue

red

green

orange

purple

Match colors.

red

black

yellow

orange

pink

 white

 blue

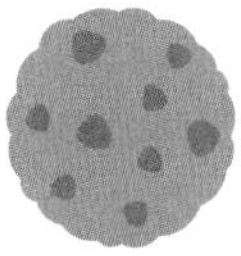

 green

 purple

 brown

Write the beginning letter.

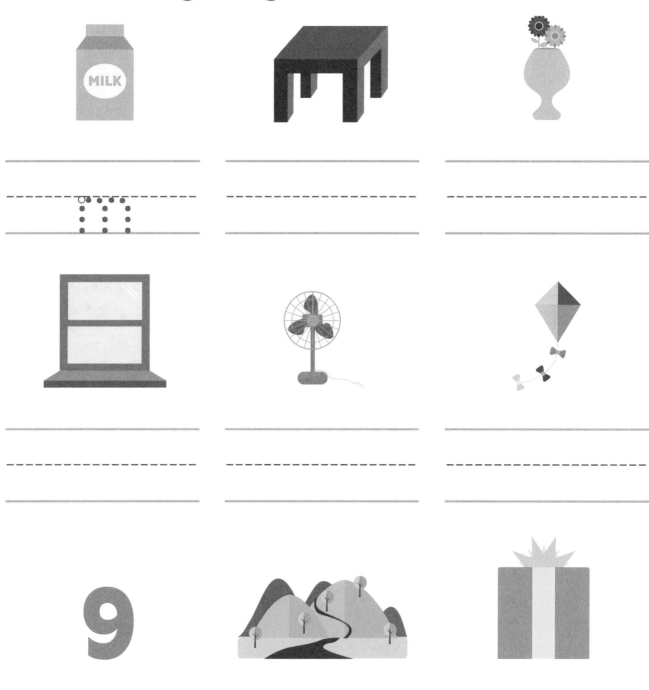

Practice z Z.

z

0

zero

zebra

Z Z Z Z

Z Z Z Z

Z Z

Z

Zion

Zebedee

Z Z Z Z

Z Z

Zz

What sound does z make?

zipper

zoo

zebra

zero

zig-zag

buzz

Listen for z.
Can you find more?

My Zz page.

zebra

Look!

Circle the answers.

Draw a line from left to right.

I can run.

A dog can run.

We can run.

Learn short vowels.

a e i o u

Circle the letter.

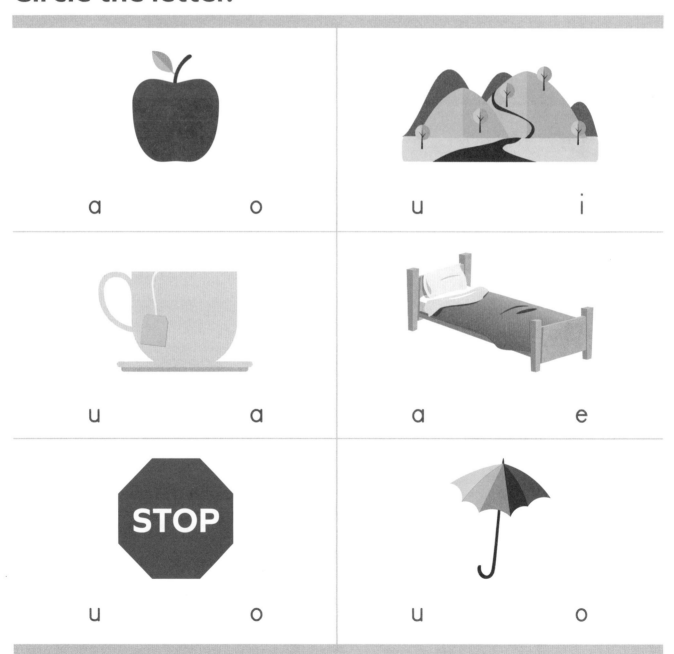

a   o   u   i

u   a   a   e

u   o   u   o

Practice q Q.

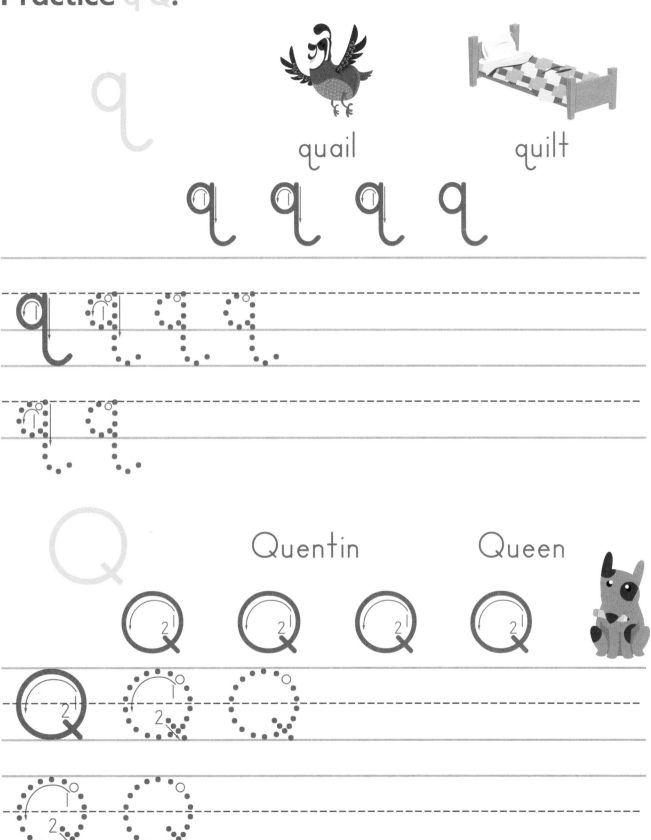

quail

quilt

Quentin

Queen

Qq

/Qq/ has a friend, /u/, that helps it speak.
What sound do they make together?
Does it sound like /kw/?

queen

question

quarter

quack

quail

quilt

Listen for /qu/.

Can you find more?

My Qq page.

Match the letters.

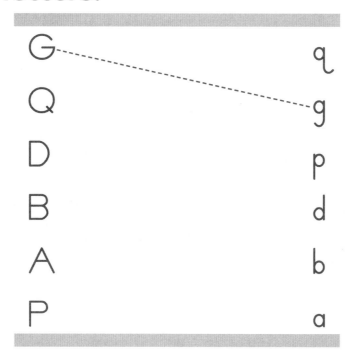

G	q
Q	g
D	p
B	d
A	b
P	a

Circle the words.

R	(Red)	man	Right	name
M	Not	Mother	Why	My
p	go	pat	pan	dog
n	no	me	red	name
m	me	name	my	who
N	Me	No	What	Now
r	now	many	red	run
P	Pat	Rose	Put	Big

Circle the letter.

c r	h g
h j	s n
s j	l m
b c	k t

Draw the patterns.

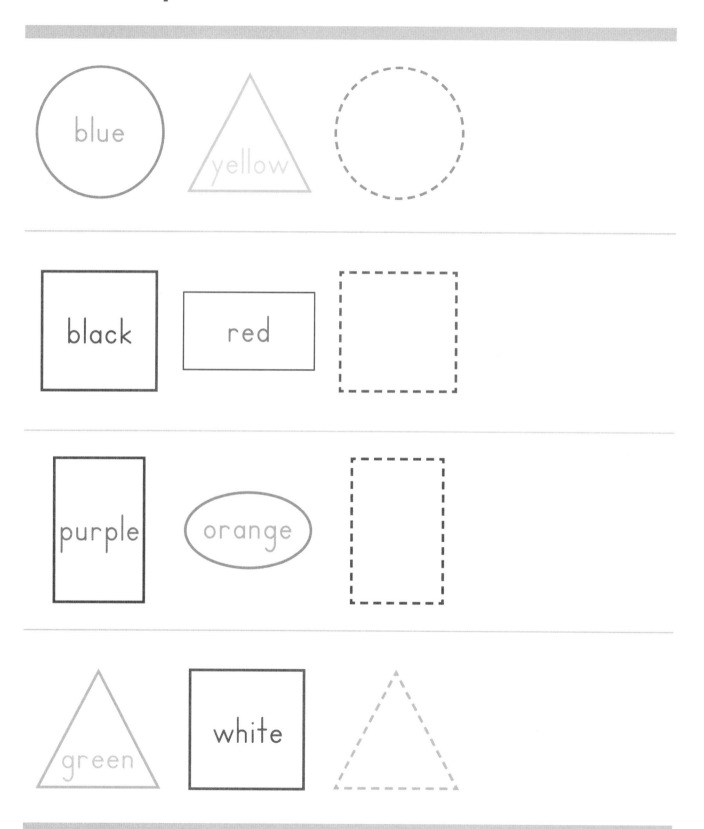

Practice x X.

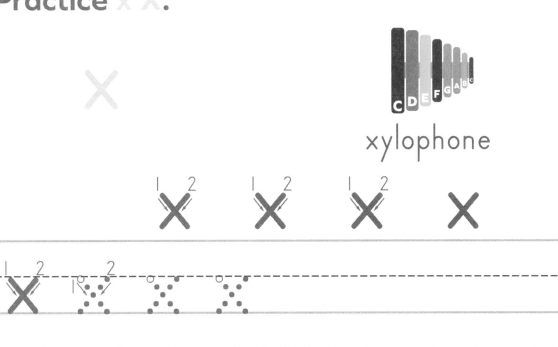

xylophone

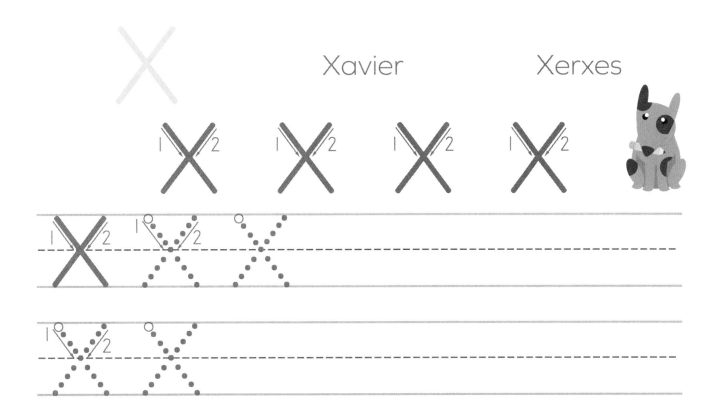

Xavier   Xerxes

**X makes two sounds. Can you say them?
One sounds like <u>ks</u>.**

x⁻ray

6
six

box

One sounds like <u>z</u>.

xylophone

Can you find more?

My Xx page.

Say the alphabet.
Write the missing letters.

a   b   _____   d   e

_____   g   h   _____   j

k   l   _____   n   o

p   _____   r   _____   t

u   _____   w   x

_____   z

Circle the letter.

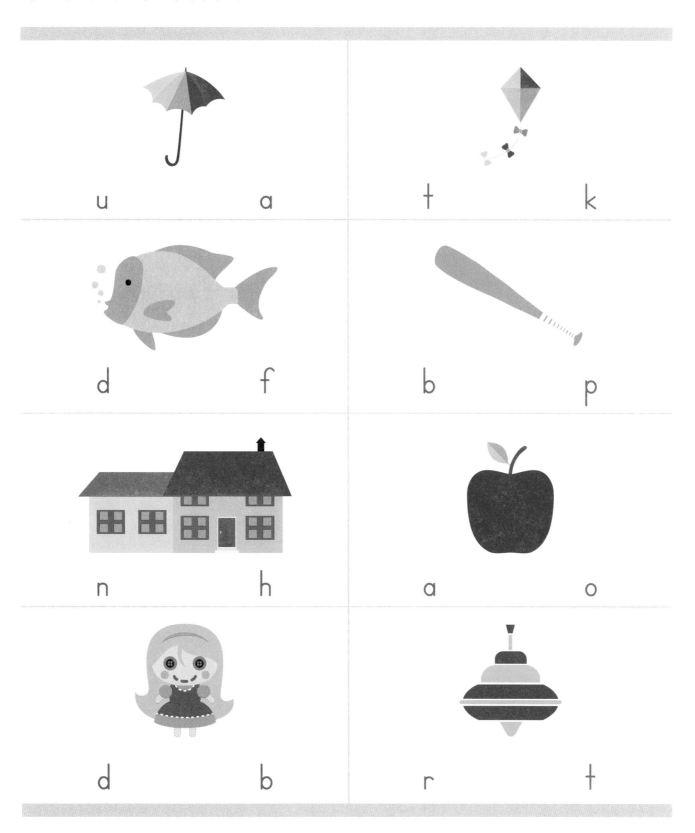

u   a   t   k

d   f   b   p

n   h   a   o

d   b   r   t

Listen and do.

WRITING PRACTICE

Let's write.

I'm ready!

abcdefghijklmnop

qrstuvwxyz

ABCDEFGHI

JKLMNOPQR

STUVWXYZ

Trace and write circles.

Trace and write.

Trace and write.

Trace and write.

Trace and write.

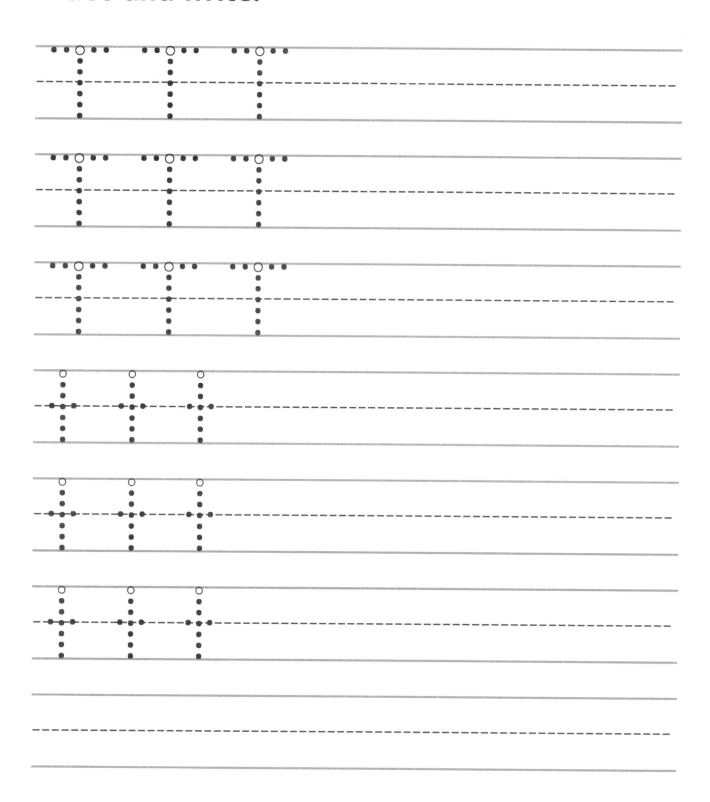

Trace and write.

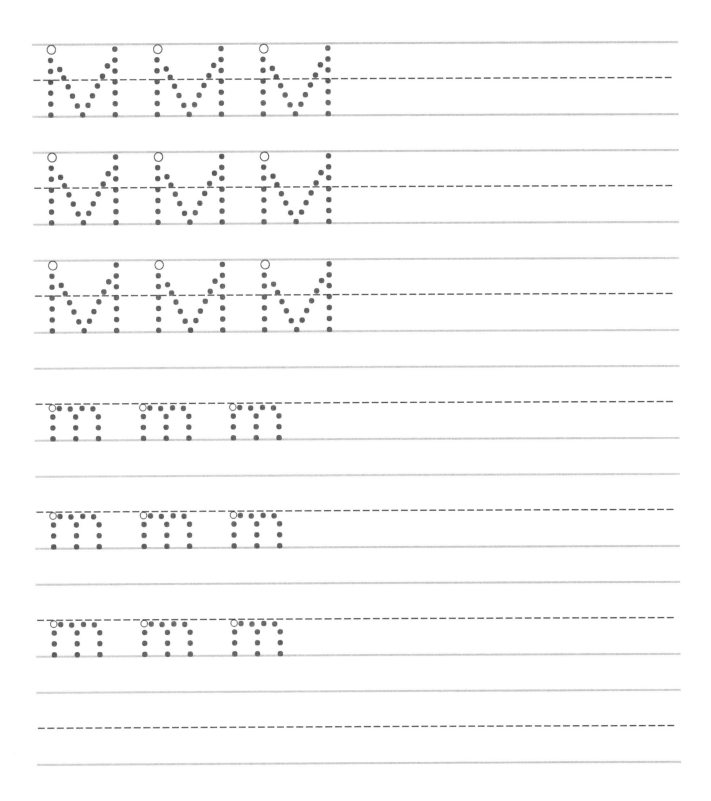

Trace and write.

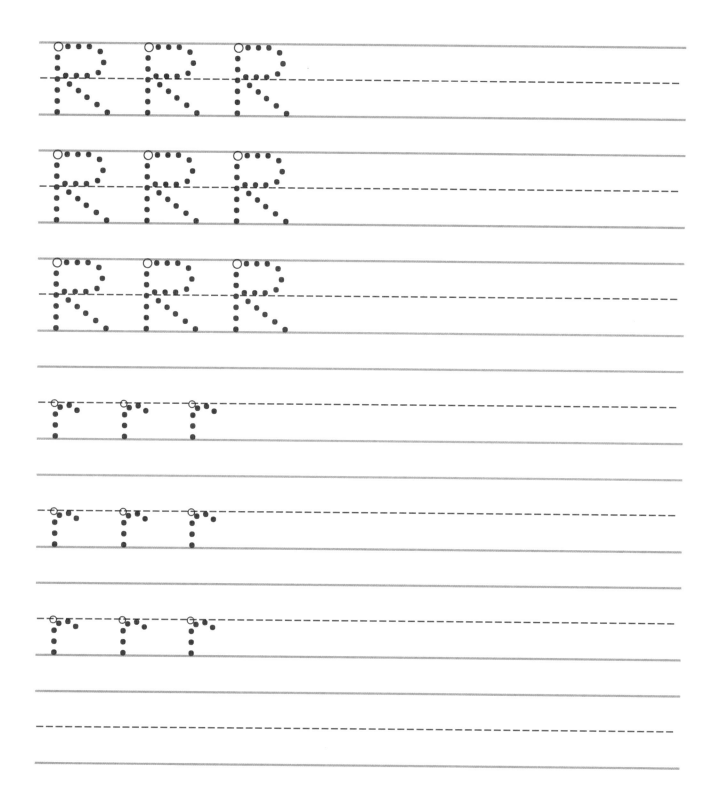

Trace and write.

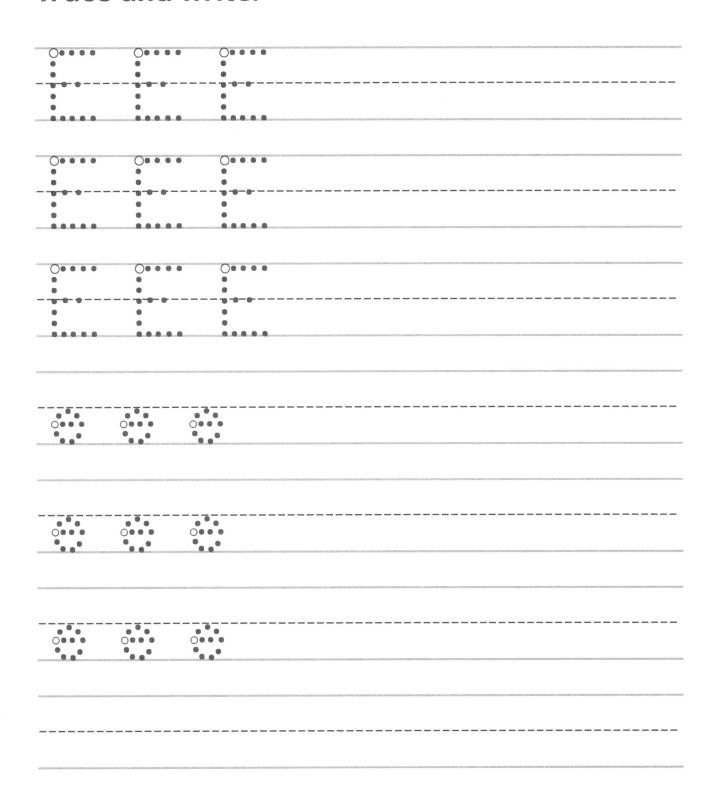

Trace and write.

Trace and write.

Trace and write.

Trace and write.

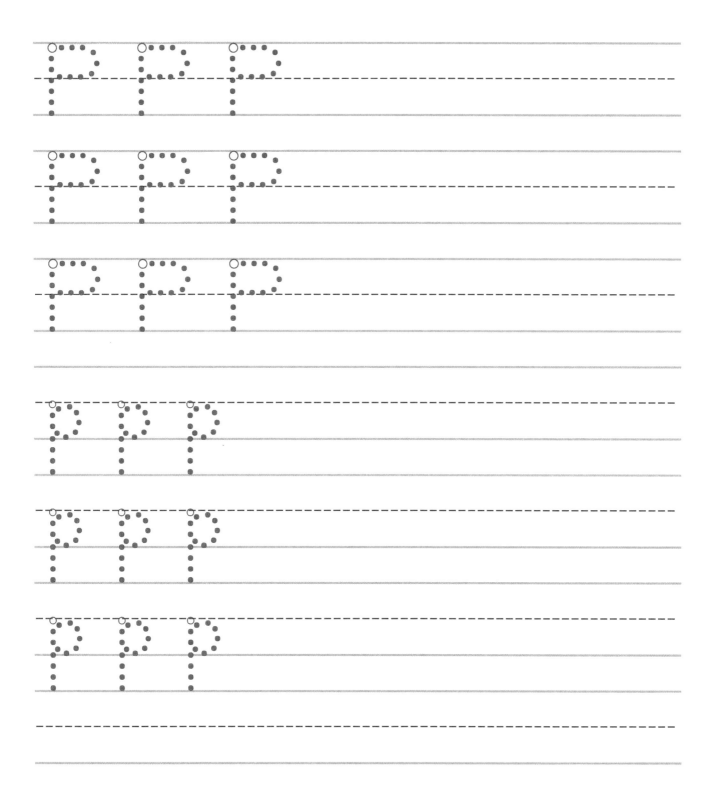

Trace and write.

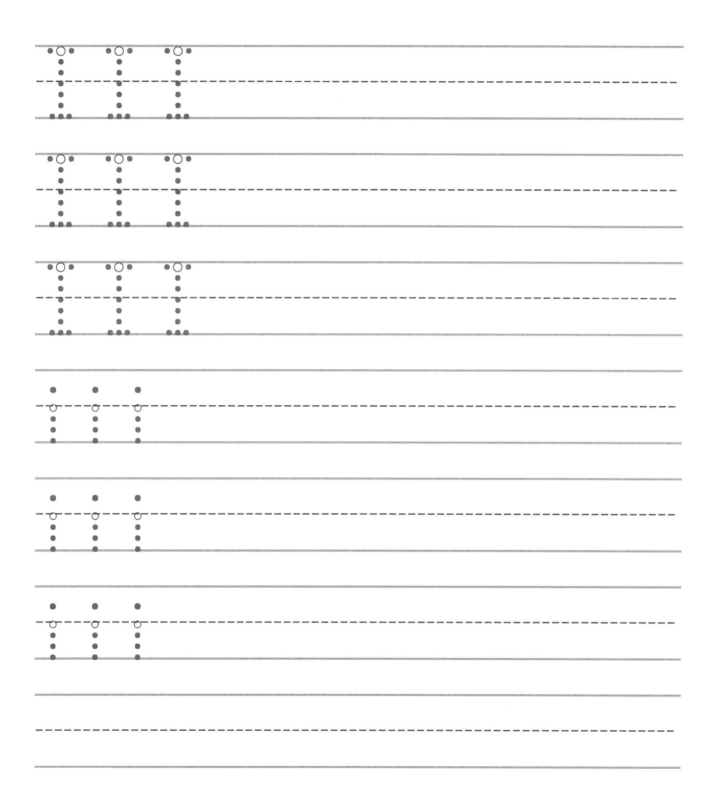

Trace and write.

Trace and write.

Trace and write.

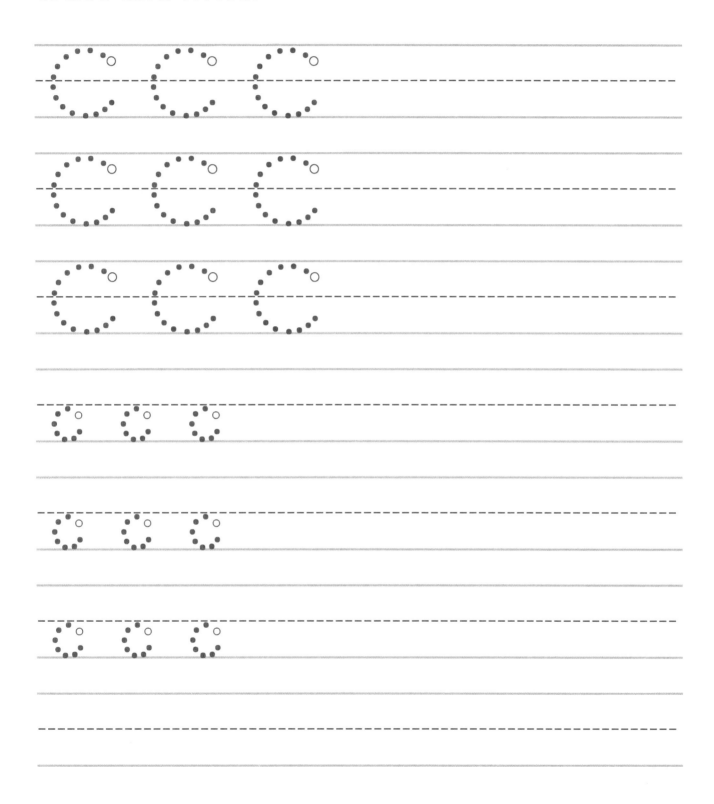

Trace and write.

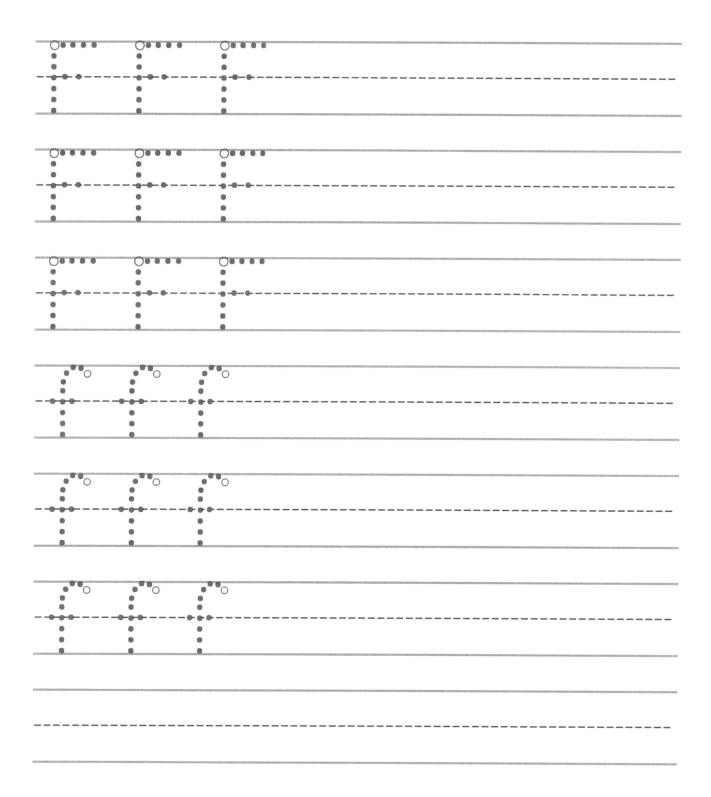

Trace and write.

Trace and write.

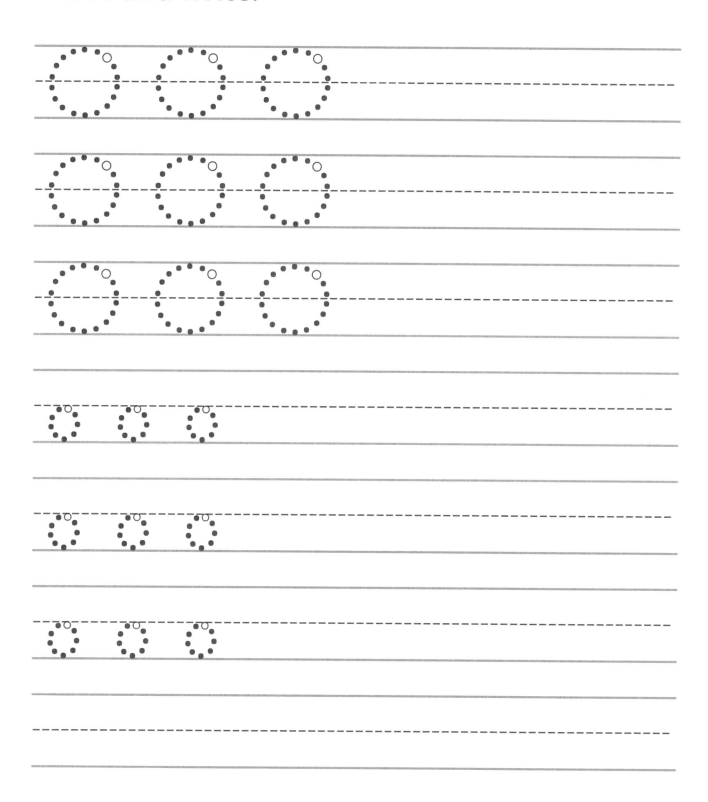

Trace and write.

Trace and write.

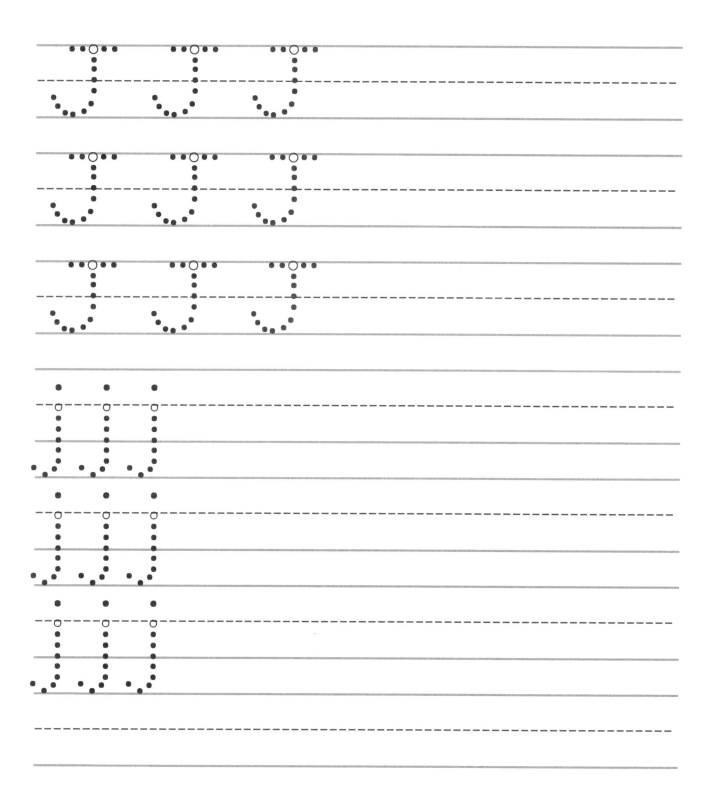

Trace and write.

Trace and write.

Trace and write.

Trace and write.

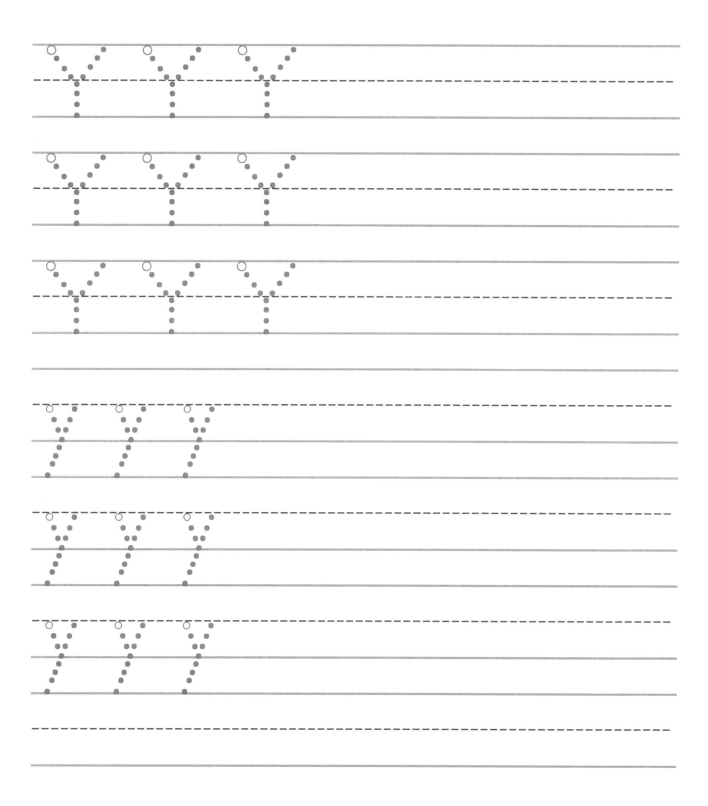

Trace and write.

Trace and write.

Trace and write.

STORY LOG

I want to read!

Me too!

Stories we read together.

Stories we read together.

Stories we read together.

Stories we read together.

My Stories

by

_____

- -

_____